GIANT CRYPTIC CROSSWORD BOOK

No. 5

ISBN 0 85144 652 3

Published by Harmsworth Magazines Ltd.,
London WC2B 5TB

© Copyright 1993 Morley Adams Ltd.
and Harmsworth Magazines Ltd.

Reprinted from past issues of the Daily Mail

Distributed by: Comag, Tavistock Road, West Drayton,
Middlesex UB7 7QE (Newstrade)
and Biblios, Partridge Green, Sussex RH13 8LD
(book trade)

Typeset by DatIX International Ltd, Bungay, Suffolk
Printed in Australia by McPherson's Printing Group

1

ACROSS

1 It's what we all think (6, 7)
8 Is he free to get off? (4)
9 Name a knight (3)
10 The case of the fruit filling (6)
11 It's not very bright to stay on through the small hours (5-5)
13 You get quite a lot from a good one (4)
14 Take note before giving it to a man for fruit (6)
16 So hot as to be highly disapproved of (8)
19 Part of the castle remaining — just follow the traffic instruction! (4, 4)
22 The sort of band that comes back after a stretch (6)
25 Timeless communication out of order (4)
26 Harbour's opening on the coast (10)
27 Ask in six to meet Ted endlessly (6)
28 Something constrictive round one's neck? (3)
29 His turn to start navigating (4)
30 Where you're not likely to find a straight face? (6, 7)

DOWN

1 Mimi's music master (7)
2 Is killing his business? (7)
3 Need Colin turn out to have so little go? (9)
4 The sphere of the regalia (3)
5 Material to work on as a contribution to the collection? (5)
6 His share dealings are not approved (7)
7 Ivan ran around in a blissful state! (7)
12 Note the rubbish in all that splendour (7)
15 Round the neck making a getaway difficult? (3)
17 Anticipate the Foreign Office gives the others everything (9)
18 The point of one's writing (3)
20 The way to get slim or make a name (7)
21 Going by without fail (7)
23 Honour in a new wife is a platitude (7)
24 Where the river makes its main impact (7)
26 The bit one might say (5)
28 You're sure of getting what's in it (3)

	¹P	U	²B	L	³I	C	⁴O	P	⁵I	N	⁶I	O	⁷N
	U		U		N		R		N		N		A
⁸S	C	O	T		⁹D	U	B		¹⁰S		S		R
	C		C		O				F		I		V
¹¹N	I	G	H	T	L	I	¹²G	H	T		¹³D	A	L
	N		E		E		L		E		E		N
¹⁴C	I	¹⁵T	R	O	N		¹⁶I	N	¹⁷F	E	R	¹⁸N	A	L
		I			C		T		A		I		
¹⁹K	²⁰E	²¹E	P	L	E	F	T		²²R	U	²³B	²⁴B	E	R
		A					E		E			S	
²⁵		²¹S		²⁶P	O	R	T	S	M	O	U	T	H
		S		I					T			U	
²⁷I	N	V	I	T	²⁸E	²⁸B	O	B		²⁹		A	
		I		C					L			R	
	³⁰		G		E					L			Y	

VENECONIA

BRIDE

BRO_IDE

I_A

2

ACROSS

1 Feeling unconscious desire, one takes it (8, 4)
8 It's written when one's starting to make one's name (7)
9 Does it give sweet pleasure to the Turks? (7)
11 Put new life into a tired name somehow (10)
12 Endless book jacket note that isn't quite clear (4)
14 Spend long periods going from room to room? (8)
16 Infuriate in sporting fashion? (4, 2)
17 The don't-care strike (3)
19 Aim to get after Jack (6)
21 Do small creatures take in the Italian at home? (8)
24 Get very hot in a painful place (4)
25 A chap turning in uses a secretary (10)
27 Nothing to hold me back but a ban! (7)
28 Not paid to prepare a rum tea (7)
29 Move metal in a dodgy way (5, 3, 4)

DOWN

1 Turns to higher things (7)
2 Gets rid of a priest taking half a minute over a set-up (10)
3 He takes away notes in a column (8)
4 Elbows for attention (6)
5 Foreigner carrying the flag? (4)
6 Support a friend in a way that is permitted (7)
7 Absurd tip Lee found so shabby (12)
10 Force of inflation in a revolutionary transport situation (4, 8)
13 Not well to repeat that one lacks education (10)
15 Unhappy indication of what a top Egyptian's at (3)
18 Fee for giving a bashing? (8)
20 Colourful appearance after a fall (7)
22 Net said to provide a possible substitute (7)
23 Meaning to buy abroad? (6)
26 One leaves the intellect to obtain the coarse part (4)

3

ACROSS

6 Disagreeable part of the house? There could be argument here! (4, 3, 7)
9 Claiming to be Mr. Bass, one hears, in Italy (6)
10 Meaty confection of male muscle? (8)
11 Little long-eared baseball players? (8)
13 Small chap with the manner of one who will do a mischief (6)
15 Device for giving me a pound back after finishing them (6)
17 Take-over for which one may be thankful (6)
19 Lump of a girl getting work (6)
20 Outpouring of notes on a get-together (8)
22 Absent-minded little girl with crazy artist (8)
24 She used to be one of the big guns (6)
26 You can see where you've been in it (4-4, 6)

DOWN

1 Scarcely a go-ahead way to effect a transfer! (4, 4, 2, 4)
2 Not quite all there, it may be gathered (4)
3 Room for a retired skater? (6)
4 If upset live at home where it's warm (8)
5 Story of being in charge after making a record (4)
7 It's nonsense about the vehicle being strong! (6)
8 Kindly remove that old radio material! (4, 2, 4, 4)
12 Some intriguing conveyance with a lion's head (5)
14 Hopes to pick up a fare (5)
16 It gives a chap time to become quite positive (8)
18 Give the most satisfactory cry of pain! (6)
21 Fabulous Richard briefly materialising (6)
23 Act of revolution (4)
25 Such heartless rapture is hard to find! (4)

4

ACROSS

1 He made a big discovery when he went west (8)
5 He acts as if pure (6)
9 Heavenly subject! (8)
10 Entertainment announcement in song (6)
12 Is he entitled to be belted? (4)
13 Your thoughts are an open book to him (4-6)
15 Amplifying device for probing the directors' thoughts? (8-5)
19 Two drinks to improve one's vision? (4, 2, 7)
23 Curved as a circle that's very thin (10)
25 Just not dark (4)
28 Shortly New York mail is diverted to a great extent (6)
29 Don's head in wrong library causes coarse merriment (8)
30 Way to take the air below (6)
31 Discourage taking in tin when you've a bottle (8)

DOWN

1 Old chap taking a man up to fish (6)
2 Food for a TV bird? (5)
3 Way out of a red city for fur (4)
4 Having no experience of the dock? (7)
6 He will find a way shortly to push (5)
7 Time for green stuff in one's youth (5, 4)
8 Older version causing some fuss in the land of dreams (2, 6)
11 Two ways to leave the country garden (4)
14 Half the junk refused by the queenly type (4)
15 Revolutionary move amid sea spray (9)
16 No good as a small drawing (3)
17 What rubbish there is in Jumbo's house! (4)
18 Mixing spice with people for example (8)
20 Boast a turn-up in dress (4)
21 A vehicle I have not found complimentary (7)
22 Petitioner or what he offers (6)
24 Worth finishing you off in the hollow (5)
26 Check what sort of ale there might be (5)
27 A delay setting up a festival (4)

5

ACROSS

1 She moves the food receptacle about to entertain (5-6)
9 It's applied to end debate (7)
10 Does he impart knowledge of British Rail procedure? (7)
11 It can't be the true position (3)
12 Having picked up some dirt from the flats, maybe (7)
13 Metal means of facilitating movement (7)
14 It gets an ovation when something new is revealed (3)
15 Animal joint on the river (5)
17 Played with a childish gift? (5)
18 Friends and assistants (5)
20 Hurried to church briefly where some beef may be raised (5)
22 Everything finally owed if permitted (3)
24 Census official going the opposite way? (7)
25 Wanted a respectful address in action (7)
26 It may get a break in spring (3)
27 Gaped even more when we'd dine informally (7)
28 A big red manoeuvre (7)
29 Here, what goes up will come down, it's projected (6-5)

DOWN

1 As violent, noisy writing it's sensational! (5-3-7)
2 Soul hit in crude form (7)
3 Give up what may be gathered (5)
4 Time a girl got pipped (9)
5 Talk about port transport (7)
6 Rapid escape from spinsterhood? (7, 8)
7 Rascal one encountered in a restaurant (6)
8 Nourished with fish inside to look shabby (6)
16 Bird bit between furrows (9)
18 Birds found the Scot was different (6)
19 Ian's act takes a devilish turn (7)
21 Mercenary of the cloth? (7)
23 Such a nice young man! (6)
25 Artist comes up with a piece of furniture to keep out (5)

6

ACROSS

1 Sold one damaged to some fools (7)
5 Stand-in for Doctor Foster (6)
9 Yes-men not venturing to speak? (7)
10 No object, perhaps, when funds are unlimited (7)
11 High point reached by some of the best ordinary shares (3)
12 Agreed procedures at meetings? (11)
13 Give him the money! (5)
14 Kept from being let out in advance (9)
16 Brief stunt deficiency (9)
17 Compete on points that can be seen (5)
19 Punishing pieces of writing (11)
22 She finishes one state and starts another (3)
23 Wild boy swallowing an animal (7)
24 Top person about to curl the lip when a writer appears (7)
26 Such a blooming tribute to the departed! (6)
27 Chap taken to wild rage when he's in charge (7)

DOWN

1 Continually going on with no poles at the highest level (3, 4)
2 Has he earned two stripes for neatness? (7, 8)
3 Fish rising on the side (3)
4 There's something warm about a country for her (5)
5 Bit of dinner? Not all at once (9)
6 Drank up at the warehouse (5)
7 We're all in it if we're quick (4, 2, 3, 6)
8 Tenanted with some facility inside (6)
12 Revolutionary and saint at the front (5)
14 Capital little credit arrangement that works well (9)
15 We ourselves find the little chaps quite conclusive (5)
16 Robert's patient teacher (6)
18 Strut about with a cane? (7)
20 Weekend started a brief year as a woman-chaser (5)
21 Pick of prison occupations (5)
25 Hurry up and come to the point! (3)

7

ACROSS

1 Calculation from beyond the grave? (4-9)
8 The way one takes note out East (4)
9 Put seed down for an animal (3)
10 Go out of one's way to entertain (6)
11 Take over the business when a stammering fellow meets an animal (10)
13 Assembly to talk of food? (4)
14 Female tutor in North London (6)
16 Embellish when there's time to make a speech (8)
19 He has an obstinate responsibility (8)
22 Beverage of the gods (6)
25 It's something you may have thought of (4)
26 Commonly occurring with winning effect? (10)
27 Author of exam paper, the dog? (6)
28 Something in it? Rubbish! (3)
29 Snack leading to a catch (4)
30 MI6 starting undercover tennis? (6, 7)

DOWN

1 Arrange to end the sitting? (7)
2 Afraid Capone had a gun (7)
3 Sounding as if it may be near Scone (9)
4 Reduce to bovine subservience (3)
5 Command some degree of rank (5)
6 He fights his way inside (7)
7 Grant me some form of cover (7)
12 Sign on as a supporter? (7)
15 Nothing reducing the length of the river (3)
17 There's probably something in it (9)
18 Inclined to a short point (3)
20 Uniform for take-off? (7)
21 Transaction raised with a movement that can be stretched (7)
23 Crib oil to get around and see a bird (7)
24 She takes lace in advance payment (7)
26 Bring together to hold the money (5)
28 Many of us might be carried away by it (3)

8

ACROSS

1 Upset by queen's lust in a later period (12)
8 Taking nothing but metal in the wood (7)
9 Irreverent little devil giving ten to you and me! (7)
11 Thinking about how the wheels go round? (10)
12 Last letter to be incorporated in metal (4)
14 One who speaks as he sees? (8)
16 Humiliate the churchman who has taken me in (6)
17 Show an agreeable lack of vigilance (3)
19 Resisting at the front? (6)
21 Seize the first in the channel (8)
24 Space for mass killing (4)
25 Depending on the people sent (10)
27 It shows what one can do with a needle (7)
28 Ironise so as to be heard more easily (7)
29 Shocking colour! (8, 4)

DOWN

1 Finds cadging an absorbing occupation? (7)
2 Cruel enough to take the skin off? (10)
3 Score minus two (8)
4 We're at one in this (6)
5 You've got it in the neck! (4)
6 One of the Popes looking like a beast? (7)
7 Accommodating build-up (5, 2, 5)
10 Disposition to be an assistant that comes easily? (6, 6)
13 Very little money to arrange a Lenin celebration (10)
15 Stick for sport (3)
18 Help to rise with a drink according to the natural scale (8)
20 Sweet conveyance to a badly arranged meal (7)
22 Copying an animal that copies (3-4)
23 It gives one the shudders (6)
26 Drink goes to Charlie's head and makes him smart (4)

9

ACROSS

6 Someone else's achievement looking good in the mirror? (9, 5)
9 Not accustomed to mint condition? (6)
10 You can tell when the bill seems odd (8)
11 It might cover one for the ceremony (8)
13 Fearfully anticipating an air force attack (6)
15 Quite a comedown to eat such pie (6)
17 Having the believer's vision (6)
19 Fishy type carrying on giving you the picture, maybe (6)
20 Interfered with mad Peter's movements (8)
22 Only one could be so strange! (8)
24 Feast on the bed (6)
26 Failed to come together without falling out (6, 2, 6)

DOWN

1 Very nice royalty from Cinderella (6, 8)
2 Notes the way up for small creatures (4)
3 Interfere with what sounds like an award (6)
4 Good enough or just enough (8)
5 In the ear of one dismissed, perhaps (4)
7 Characteristics of the wild artist (6)
8 They put things right on the move (7, 7)
12 The man with the gun (5)
14 River of gold (5)
16 She takes the money when one digs (8)
18 It's sound to steer the wrong way by the roundabout (6)
21 He sees with the spirit (6)
23 Its monarch is a beast! (4)
25 Wildfire spread far and wide (4)

10

ACROSS

1 Trophy on a plank behind the door (8)
5 Comes clean? (6)
9 Come together to study on the side (8)
10 Accommodation he lost in the confusion (6)
12 Good subject for a wish (4)
13 Something attempted, something done (10)
15 Cheap horse seen in the sales? (7, 6)
19 Cruelly apply soap and water? (5, 4, 4)
23 Something to do when you've sat up (4, 6)
25 Don't go on bringing vessels back (4)
28 Acts the miser — it's so hard to change! (6)
29 Reduce speed following the fashion (8)
30 Easy catch for the artist? (6)
31 He wants to find the girl after cares are dispersed (8)

DOWN

1 Heart-warming little creature (6)
2 Terror of a god (5)
3 Nothing to write to start with (4)
4 Craft gathering (7)
6 A business with the Navy providing the oak (5)
7 Sizzling number to a kid of an African (9)
8 As wholesome as touching one's cap? (8)
11 French bread causing discomfort (4)
14 Work worry (4)
15 The dog's is a mess! (9)
16 It may be well provided (3)
17 One thing you can count on (4)
18 In which one's laughing heartily, though needled? (8)
20 Spot one and turn up to start arguing (4)
21 Fence in some of the men near (7)
22 Seem to come into view? (6)
24 Make contact to gain attention (5)
26 Turn right over before reaching the tree — rubbish! (5)
27 Carry a note into the saloon (4)

11

ACROSS

1 Is it used for weighing money when you've something put away? (4, 7)
9 Let care be dispersed by sweetness! (7)
10 You'd be crazy to go it! (7)
11 Exist in a backward age (3)
12 Followed the line Mr. Heath has taken in (7)
13 Cocky creature taking a rest? (7)
14 One way a short announcement may cause tears (3)
15 Praise formerly getting much in return (5)
17 Speed at which ship ties up? (5)
18 It helps to give one flexible standing (5)
20 Poet giving contradictory answers (5)
22 Car crashing into a bend (3)
24 Homely sort of pie? (7)
25 His aquatic achievements earned a Hero's welcome (7)
26 Light comedian? (3)
27 Told by one of the family (7)
28 Particular esteem? (7)
29 More learning that's not of the best? (6-5)

DOWN

1 Knocking it back, knocking them down — all that was the good life! (4, 3, 8)
2 Housing for fliers (7)
3 The gift of prayer (5)
4 Like Mr. Steel in generous mood? (9)
5 Refuse to contact the right people in the county (7)
6 Propaganda indicating where the committee rooms are? (8, 7)
7 Such a symbol as might establish one's position (6)
8 Gets round what a girl wears? (6)
16 A number might be rented in Kent (9)
18 One has us acting together (6)
19 Can be given extended treatment (7)
21 Bird on the water in port (7)
23 Bill takes him to be right (6)
25 Billy Richards has it in him to write the words (5)

12

ACROSS

1 If cited may result in a loss (7)
5 Want to put you in the river, dear fellow! (6)
9 He was wise to be on his own one day (7)
10 Ray's held off when it's put up (7)
11 Help a girl who's lost her head (3)
12 Device for transferring print on coat (11)
13 Vision of the night (5)
14 Rising fixtures? (9)
16 Misuse the box after scattering seed (9)
17 In which a very poor performer may be clapped (5)
19 Offering more for a lot (11)
22 Send back over a player's head (3)
23 He loves to feel money doesn't matter (7)
24 One who gets something from a late departure (7)
26 Inclined to have a man around at last (6)
27 Storm drama (7)

DOWN

1 Break up the orchestra? (7)
2 A lot of talk about what to wear? (4-5, 6)
3 Scot turning up in the river (3)
4 Saw a number added (5)
5 Going for something different (9)
6 It might have a hanger-on in transport (5)
7 Chance of getting shot in the Red revolution (7, 8)
8 Slaps down the boards (6)
12 Funny business with a bit of mickey taking (5)
14 Need dream have been shattered when one failed to go straight? (9)
15 Unidentified object (5)
16 Adder coiled round a ring in the tree (6)
18 It might cause talk (7)
20 Its winner is a family supporter (5)
21 Land in the water — has permission (5)
25 Swot up Arabic possibly (3)

13

ACROSS

1 How smart colourful plumage may be repeated? (6, 7)
8 Shorten to look neat (4)
9 Ready to get back if there's a check (3)
10 Survivor of a partnership (6)
11 Speculative country brought to book? (10)
13 Outpouring in a pub not at all angry (4)
14 The holy woman might be quite another girl (6)
16 How the cards may be stiffened (8)
19 Darling of the younger generation (8)
22 Somebody taking a chance to become superior? (6)
25 Cause a storm in a teacup (4)
26 As worn by slap-happy entertainers (10)
27 Stay and see about the pipe (6)
28 Do its members plead for drinks? (3)
29 It's hard to take another way (4)
30 The fun of getting rid of one's money! (8, 5)

DOWN

1 Claim to show the meaning (7)
2 Make a new style with regard to the sitter (7)
3 Braves not turning out to be very watchful (9)
4 In good shape for a start? (3)
5 Just a little bit to keep the communist quiet (5)
6 Such religion is making a different claim (7)
7 Housing in the air (7)
12 Confident the fool will be given a rude shaking (7)
15 Give me a turn before you finish a layer (3)
17 Warning light on stormy rigs provided by a big swimmer (9)
18 Not easy to handle (3)
20 Bill needs hair to portray a stage female (7)
21 Relevant foreigner taking the point (7)
23 The pig in extremity can be a brisk mover (7)
24 Give a lift (7)
26 Given marks for good writing (5)
28 Something to eat in town with gay abandon (3)

14

ACROSS

1 Revolutionary line to make one jumpy? (8, 4)
8 One seems to have got somewhere on this (7)
9 It's what you'd expect to see in some dump (7)
11 Act on flair that may be erratic in part (10)
12 Quite good at describing a blonde? (4)
14 Little girls to identify officials? (8)
16 One isn't free to go under this (6)
17 It may be seen to be infuriating (3)
19 Getting something done, one takes it (6)
21 Winds lead to a fall on the runway (8)
24 One call for repetition may get you the bird (4)
25 No female allowed to be such a small creature? (4-6)
27 Significance of sound and fury (7)
28 Gains from former wrongs (7)
29 Absorb too much of Paris? (3, 9)

DOWN

1 Goes quickly along exposed lines? (7)
2 Party membership — that would be asking! (10)
3 Garment seen when the drawing is finished (8)
4 It's quite usual to knock a fellow up (6)
5 Girl in red (4)
6 The unknown soldier? (7)
7 Fault attributable, perhaps, to a Roman film (12)
10 Fastidious enough to appreciate firmness? (4, 2, 6)
13 Seeker after hidden wealth (10)
15 The muddled ones are all at it! (3)
18 The least attractive form of dietings (8)
20 Showing how prickly the Scots can be? (7)
22 Having stopped work and gone to bed? (7)
23 Mark the way a soldier turns up with the old lady (6)
26 Slip of the tongue? (4)

15

ACROSS

6 In a heavenly orbit? (3, 2, 4, 5)
9 Bathroom cake? (6)
10 Opening for a purer tea blend (8)
11 Meant to get in and be looked after (8)
13 Weaver at the lowest level (6)
15 Gear seized beyond the exit (6)
17 Go away when Red Pat looks revolutionary! (6)
19 Ghost of a feeling? (6)
20 Being the person he is, he's not here (8)
22 Worldly little office worker taking an exam (8)
24 Commemorative dinner? (6)
26 Its coming was nominally the end of old Bob (7, 7)

DOWN

1 The bit you have with you? (9, 5)
2 Money put up for a crop (4)
3 Cause annoyance by going beyond the limit (6)
4 See lambs somehow get together (8)
5 Run away with some cloth? (4)
7 Amasses multitudes of sound (6)
8 The Prince of Wales in Scotland (4, 2, 3, 5)
12 Take up an inside position (5)
14 Moving aspect of the bride's appearance? (5)
16 Art linen folded and put down inside (8)
18 Call GI to assembly in French (6)
21 Make a big effort to show breeding (6)
23 Personal assistant in a display of ill-feeling (4)
25 Scheme to reveal the layout (4)

16

ACROSS

1 Area providing scope for a nurse (8)
5 Makes proud progress as the supporters demonstrate (6)
9 Ray's mine when school breaks up! (8)
10 Setting business up and getting on — that's the ticket! (6)
12 Call all round (4)
13 There's such pressure to say what the weather's doing! (10)
15 Buckingham Palace on investiture day? (5, 2, 6)
19 It's too wild to be one of the herd (5, 8)
23 Splendid position for watching sport (10)
25 Man with business in the street (4)
28 Like a dog that's wandered off (6)
29 Measure of poetry there might be in a quart (8)
30 By no means fortuitously difficult (6)
31 Not afraid to get in and mince tripe before dinner starts (8)

DOWN

1 Run away from the lush landscape? (6)
2 He'll gain foreign agreement one day (5)
3 Very poor standing? (4)
4 Mind taking a horse in for slaughter (7)
6 Found to be treasure (5)
7 Prepare supper with Tom at the head (9)
8 It pays not to work very hard (8)
11 Beastly leader of the Mozart gang (4)
14 In which there's no danger of losing money? (4)
15 Show time in butler's room (9)
16 Poetry in the modern way (3)
17 All-round prohibition in Scotland (4)
18 He boasts finally with gravity and skill (8)
20 Instrument of friendship? (4)
21 King of the Antarctic (7)
22 Good man having done wrong to be squiffy (6)
24 Empty artist in a row (5)
26 Painful restraint (5)
27 Cause trouble in prison? (4)

17

ACROSS

1 Beast with a hiding-place in the pub (4, 3, 4)
9 There's a lot of growth potential in this (7)
10 Means of destroying one ship in the distance (7)
11 The way Brenda starts to cry (3)
12 Gets boats in trouble (7)
13 It may be after one thing (7)
14 Old-fashioned agreement (3)
15 Permit to get a ham in Lincolnshire (5)
17 Loop a ring in the nostrils (5)
18 Check what the treasurer says (5)
20 She puts her boy first (5)
22 Payment for finishing drink (3)
24 Boy meets bird — that's the way it's arranged (7)
25 He charges the employer after getting a short measure (7)
26 Liable to shorten a point (3)
27 Drawing a vehicle to get on (7)
28 Working hard to take one fish (7)
29 Where tobacco commercials are shown to hide what's happening? (5-6)

DOWN

1 Uncertain way to begin in the tailoring trade? (2, 4, 3, 6)
2 End of a flight at home or at the airport (7)
3 Bay storm taking ship into unfathomable chaos (5)
4 Unspeakable skill at getting on in Scotland (9)
5 Now runs around without being bounded by oath (7)
6 Latest thing for the smart climber? (6, 2, 7)
7 Trade in church jobs? It ought to be simple! (6)
8 Does it show how hot one is at learning? (6)
16 One can ass around in similarity of sound (9)
18 Look at a bit of a gamble inside (6)
19 Musically it gives one the shivers! (7)
21 Attribute to a writer (7)
23 Infuriate the paper in one direction (6)
25 Such accommodating wit? (5)

18

ACROSS

1 Name ten with us who are not sure (7)
5 They're likely to get talked about (6)
9 More than a little of what you fancy (7)
10 Urge Don to change and suffer (7)
11 Quite a fuss in the publicity circle (3)
12 Lose standing with too much money in the bank? (11)
13 Undesirable encountered in low-life London (5)
14 Any repast prepared for country folk (9)
16 We won't be together after this (9)
17 Bitter greetings, we hear (5)
19 Such a chap has done it before (11)
22 Bone to spare possibly (3)
23 It depends on the listener (3-4)
24 Time for the senior officer to be right at the front (7)
28 Heavenly body in remote orbit (6)
27 Bird on the water in town (7)

DOWN

1 I'd turn up with employees on the ladies' side (7)
2 It holds unlimited funds for the spender (10, 5)
3 A person who isn't named (3)
4 The fashionable way of doing things (5)
5 Little Tom is one to pin down such a sketch (9)
6 Put your foot down forcefully and repeatedly (5)
7 Crowning clobber (10, 5)
8 Looking like Eros? (6)
12 You can tell how much Ann has put on (5)
14 He's no help in keeping things going (9)
15 Prize for a protege (5)
16 Go on digging the river enclosure (6)
18 One way part of Europe can be put beyond the Urals (7)
20 River of gold (5)
21 Go over to make your mark (5)
25 Not all the players provide refreshment (3)

19

ACROSS

1 It gives one pull as a marksman (7, 6)
8 An additional message is to the point in church (4)
9 All-round feature of the sitter? (3)
10 Spike comes back after taking a bit of a line for the lady (6)
11 Does he carry out work to reduce the size? (10)
13 Put down fifty with help (4)
14 Not much room to manoeuvre in a difficulty (6)
16 He wasn't there a little while ago (8)
19 The seducer puts a salver in the drink (8)
22 Line of pressure (6)
25 One might learn from putting this much on (4)
26 It may be taken from those in service (10)
27 Muster in a dud formation (6)
28 Instrument for removing the heart of a weasel (3)
29 With "25" she's unsparing (4)
30 Small heroine using communist cover? (3, 6, 4)

DOWN

1 Something to wear when going for a spin? (3-4)
2 It isn't what's required to get you going? (7)
3 Does it earn the ladies' man a medal? (9)
4 Be quick to cause some damage (3)
5 Not busy but he's riled if disturbed (5)
6 The sun stood still for him (7)
7 Understand now to raise cash (7)
12 Shoot a climber (7)
15 It has a suspicious smell (3)
17 Indication that one is no longer defending the colours? (5, 4)
18 Sort of cap from the crowd (3)
20 He makes a constructive contribution (7)
21 Started again to put money in the plant (7)
23 Train crash between circuits in Canada (7)
24 Chosen as one of the family (7)
26 Barking firm given new rig (5)
28 He's given two degrees in popular literature (3)

20

ACROSS

1 The job of getting MPs to vote where someone may be beaten? (8-4)
8 Unpleasant changing fuel after taking cover (7)
9 Record one state that makes sense (7)
11 Taking what's left (10)
12 Danger behind the ice (4)
14 One is barely seen to be in the running (8)
16 Act to disturb the rest of the county (6)
17 Try to finish idle talk (3)
19 Unknown commander of a sect (6)
21 Organiser of career improvements? (8)
24 Girl in bed! (4)
25 Handing out the wrong design pins (10)
27 Explosive device to hand (7)
28 Gave an impression of extreme displeasure (7)
29 March enables him to show how he feels (12)

DOWN

1 He sees what's going on (7)
2 Tell a friend how to avoid ceremony (10)
3 They provide colourful backgrounds in the studios (8)
4 They cover supporting members (6)
5 Servant brought to book (4)
6 You'll do well to achieve it (7)
7 Continuous weed burning on the links? (5-7)
10 Electricity people making an exceptional charge? (5, 7)
13 Commercial shortage and a worker giving the orders (10)
15 Let go like a tearaway? (3)
18 He makes a moving speech (8)
20 He's nice in his foreign way (7)
22 Traveller of uncertain standing? (7)
23 Sundry workers in the depths (6)
26 Pudding for starters? (4)

21

ACROSS

6 Bring back music after a quarrel? (7, 7)
9 Loved to give Dora a turn with a boy (6)
10 Cries out at former demands (8)
11 Let's pray for the making of music (8)
13 The head's supporter has it all round (6)
15 Cause to draw on (6)
17 Played in groovy style? (6)
19 Concerning the body that's right in the waterway (6)
20 Hint at a pub turn that will finish with nothing on (8)
22 Dish a queasy sailor in a warship (8)
24 Signal supporter (6)
26 Setting a vision to make probes (14)

DOWN

1 In which things are fixed before you get there? (14)
2 He employs you and me with some hesitation (4)
3 Dog of a foreigner to act up inside (6)
4 Going a long way to start being ridiculous (8)
5 Some of them may well include her (4)
7 Two girls might make a man (6)
8 What entitles one to a place in the records? (4, 3, 7)
12 Burdened with the French study (5)
14 Centre of revolution in the factory (5)
16 Tie cable in single form (8)
18 Tommy's old trouble pack? (3-3)
21 Things are different in the dark! (6)
23 Right turn in a river (4)
25 Refuse approval in the recess (4)

22

ACROSS

1 Cockney time to detain a flier (4-4)
5 Climbs on a fish's back (6)
9 Fruit of the Normandy landings (8)
10 Big gun able to gain French disagreement (6)
12 What fun to be an early riser! (4)
13 Curve more than adequately for a fluttering beauty (10)
15 Picture in the football special, for instance? (8, 5)
19 Bemused Martian player of the political game (13)
23 Understand how values will rise (10)
25 Bill and that man cause discomfort (4)
28 Hang about to display it in a different role (6)
29 Simmer on in the wrong calling (8)
30 Do its articles produce a gut reaction? (6)
31 Not knowing there's a girl in the middle (8)

DOWN

1 Make a rather erratic beeline? (6)
2 Straight man at the top? (5)
3 Staffordshire's tribute to Wales? (4)
4 Doctor taking a short way with an insect biting (7)
6 One might profess to be its occupant (5)
7 It keeps one going to a greater extent than most (9)
8 Lines up with it when you begin to show the effects of age (8)
11 Catch nothing up in Scotland (4)
14 Note a West African rising in the desert (4)
15 Young streaker? (9)
16 Land anger? (3)
17 Fork out about 50 for entertainment (4)
18 Took up a lot of space lying (8)
20 Letters make the old lady almost sick (4)
21 Significance of a circle (7)
22 Undercover sappers in a group (6)
24 They give a 50-50 chance (5)
26 It gives the reader pause (5)
27 Cancel the performance? (4)

23

ACROSS

1 They may be too deep for bubbles (5, 6)
9 A Dr. Fish making some sort of progress (7)
10 Escape route for deserter (3-4)
11 Silver taken from Dutch city with a cry (3)
12 Run cart round for the fruit (7)
13 Came out and backed me with misdirected greed (7)
14 Foreign gentleman in river (3)
15 Frenchman taking a measure on the way (5)
17 The voice of meaning (5)
18 Early morning rig-out? (3-2)
20 Stout fellow, Capone, but deadly (5)
22 In which a dream castle might be built (3)
24 Make a hit with the gear? (7)
25 Not pleased at being endlessly put in peril (7)
26 There's nothing to be said for keeping her! (3)
27 Crown sceptre, big cigar? (7)
28 Swagger of Costa party? (7)
29 A soldier with a hard point can be an entertainer (5, 6)

DOWN

1 Stop drinking? What an idea! (8, 7)
2 Provide something like one way to the gallery (7)
3 Come down with a beam? (5)
4 Ten meagre amendments to contract (9)
5 Beg to have a meal after disposing of the rent (7)
6 In which a girl might acquire a double-barrelled name? (7, 8)
7 Bad state in an attack (6)
8 He'll want his own back later (6)
16 Hospital in the wood taking a girl (9)
18 Childish vehicle that will move (2-4)
19 A piece of butter in the fruit for your sustenance (7)
21 The stuff you haul around with you (7)
23 Sends for the receivers (6)
25 Morning with a piece offering some scope (5)

24

ACROSS

1 Bad rust problem for a flyer (7)
5 Opening pronouncement (6)
9 Material bit put back for the animal catcher (7)
10 Old Bob won't get fat going to a usurer (7)
11 Paul gets in after him for cover (3)
12 Tendency not to be on the level (11)
13 Extra payment for getting on in transport (5)
14 Englishman in America, or maybe a Scot (9)
16 Lad taking relations a small drink (9)
17 Maud's turn to identify writer (5)
19 They make rash singing appear better (11)
22 Animal returning for identification (3)
23 One aunt disposed of behind the driver (7)
24 It may be put up to avert defeat (7)
26 Quarrel in the wind (6)
27 Intellectual urge to a top teacher (7)

DOWN

1 One could get immersed in it at home (7)
2 He may make a hit as an associate (8, 7)
3 One might hope to put the heat on this creature (3)
4 Dialect suitable for a column? (5)
5 Under which one may be thought to have done wrong (9)
6 To some degree she names the old country (5)
7 Late and early show (8, 7)
8 The person to smooth things out (6)
12 Comes out of the dispute (5)
14 Where one might work for bread? (9)
15 Try to get off hard work in the river (5)
16 Times when one's requirements are light (6)
18 Incline to go under and be opposed? (7)
20 Ernie's quite wrong for her (5)
21 Gain attention with a note in stark form (5)
25 Small picture of fruit? (3)

25

ACROSS

1 Taking little time to add sugar? (5, 3, 5)
8 One may have it doubled (4)
9 Fool in a trench (3)
10 Business chief absorbing a conclusion (6)
11 Basis of a charitable body? (10)
13 Point to the age of light (4)
14 Declare a supporter is in drink (6)
16 It's not what one expects (8)
19 Proved the man to have a different taste (8)
22 For a pin-up this takes the cake! (6)
25 Quiet performance by agreement (4)
26 Home of a poetic lad (10)
27 Room where you can get a cool drink? (6)
28 He's quite taken in by demure Felicity (3)
29 Run along and cut off Ernie's head! (4)
30 No good if you haven't paid enough? (5, 3, 5)

DOWN

1 Is it brought by ship from Newcastle? (3-4)
2 One is not at all pleased to be given it (7)
3 You may find it in the Bible if you will (9)
4 Cloth for cards? (3)
5 Resort to find in another country (5)
6 She may be responsible for one real reform (7)
7 Going on and on giving a chap promises to pay (7)
12 He's not affected by exclusiveness (7)
15 Man who had everything? (3)
17 The party that takes you in? (9)
18 Break it to take the social plunge (3)
20 City jam maker (7)
21 Get weaving on making ten fuddled with drink (7)
23 Lets the air out (7)
24 Inclined to fight in bits and pieces? (7)
26 Going up sharply in price (5)
28 Time to add to bitterness in the old ship (3)

26

ACROSS

1 Prompt to give Austin the gin concoction (12)
8 Concentrated in a number on the Stock Exchange (7)
9 Quiet criticism before the public are admitted (7)
11 Half the world is present after he takes the imps around (10)
12 Samantha is displaying an Asian interior (4)
14 Dispatched about ten cents as a deposit (8)
16 Faithless? Don't believe it! (6)
17 Fuel in the pipe-line (3)
19 Open out and arrange some fun before you get elderly (6)
21 The cap is possibly imitative work (8)
24 What do you know? Here's a way of finding out! (4)
25 Drum and bass helping one to get the message? (3-7)
27 Well-known inn involved with the meet (7)
28 Something to take one forward on a horse (7)
29 Part of the meal taken at another track? (6, 6)

DOWN

1 Wild about that crazy aunt on the sea! (7)
2 How a male model expects to be paid? (10)
3 Watch and object coming to the boil (8)
4 Makes a point of providing lights (6)
5 Where drives start going into the sea (4)
6 Rejecting both alternatives causes confusion therein (7)
7 Not much room for a drunken embrace? (5, 7)
10 Award for cowardice (5, 7)
13 He may have a telling effect on learners (10)
15 Strike over the water? (3)
18 Arrange to gain as capital (8)
20 Easily damaged paper in the folder (7)
22 He's been caught taking the wrong tip in the grotto (7)
23 Went in not wholly dissimilar directions? (6)
26 It doesn't allow the animal man to hold the ring (4)

27

ACROSS

6 Nobody asked him to be a party member (9, 5)
9 Frightening creature to sit beside one (6)
10 Story from one of the family (8)
11 Faint-hearted Moor turning back to America after giving it back (8)
13 Not easy to make Kit cry, perhaps (6)
15 Dig out from the work of a philosopher (6)
17 His is a character-forming occupation (6)
19 Rex gets on with him as a performer (6)
20 Like a god of undying quality (8)
22 Getting round the question of what a girl might wear? (8)
24 Imagining red revolution with a girl (6)
26 Get ready to do some streaking? (5, 3, 6)

DOWN

1 Not what you expected from the postman? (8, 6)
2 One's afraid to get it up (4)
3 Make too much of the performance? (6)
4 Great admirer of what the bride says subsequently (8)
5 Floater likely to get the push (4)
7 Mavis sickness? (6)
8 Current remedy causing dismay? (5, 9)
12 One of the family loses her head — not this one! (5)
14 Put away down below (5)
16 Old lady's disagreements in the kennels (8)
18 American negotiator finally becoming an entertainer (6)
21 I'd come to be the man to give the treatment (6)
23 Fall under a cloud (4)
25 The way of the escapist (4)

28

ACROSS

1 Rod getting wet measuring the depth (3-5)
5 Home for the brave (6)
9 He's able to throw some light on his subject (8)
10 Playful meeting at the table (6)
11 Be quick to display verve (4)
13 Novel market for triviality (6, 4)
15 Occasion for striking acquaintance? Surely not? (8, 5)
19 Fine fellow to a motorist of long standing! (7, 6)
23 Given permission by the writer? (10)
25 Is it taken for outstanding performance at the tea-table? (4)
28 Like the difficult problem of Dodd's ash? (6)
29 It offers several outlets for a chap if of ripe years (8)
30 Have recourse to a holiday town (6)
31 Time for spring? (4-4)

DOWN

1 Led up with due deviation to deceive (6)
2 Questions the footwear (5)
3 A girl's top weapon (4)
4 No doubt you can make it! (7)
6 Give it to an Asian in the country (5)
7 Gain part of Switzerland at the races (9)
8 It's constitutional in Britain (8)
11 Face a display of figures (4)
14 Hit the damn fool if inside! (4)
15 Ready to quarrel over a part? (9)
16 Deposit in the early morning (3)
17 Fashion for bringing the navy up to date (4)
18 His approach is striking (8)
20 Cut at a brisk speed (4)
21 Greeting with anger that's not out of the ordinary (7)
22 First man to give a newspaper opinion? (6)
24 It's just on target! (5)
26 Lived in a home (5)
27 Move awkwardly — but without stiffness? (4)

29

ACROSS

1 Register for a job in a restaurant? (7-4)
9 Fairy with fishy attributes back in the cold (7)
10 Steps taken to make a military arrangement (7)
11 Make a point of providing a cask of ale (3)
12 Old-time agitator finding a way to get into a ship (7)
13 Gay fellows at a dance (7)
14 Time for one to change (3)
15 Points to the girl in Surrey (5)
17 Carried Mr. Heath as the dedicatee? (5)
18 Smart fellows providing five hundred in fees (5)
20 The way to display fashion (5)
22 Not even peculiar? But it is! (3)
24 Girl gets a chap in the plant (7)
25 Leaving port for sport (7)
26 The crazy one may be made tight (3)
27 Worshipped if I am in action (7)
28 Source of inflation in transport? (3-4)
29 Clay so handy in time of peace and happiness (7, 4)

DOWN

1 Moslem revolutionary? (8, 7)
2 Blow up for being tardy with some gen (7)
3 Not very clever to take in the wrong pet! (5)
4 It may go to one's head in Inverness-shire (9)
5 Take what's left in putting the girl to it (7)
6 London and Paris booking! (4, 2, 3, 6)
7 Could be employed as blue mixture (6)
8 Not accustomed to seeing an international body exploited (6)
16 Economising in marriage? (9)
18 The thing to do for success as a ruler? (6)
19 No ordinary copper (7)
21 In Africa it comes to the engineers in time (7)
23 Follower of the bank? (6)
25 Grateful when evil surrounds making a mark (5)

30

ACROSS

1 In a fog at meal-time? (3, 4)
5 Girl depressed at looking pale (6)
9 Nobody wants to know him (7)
10 Cardinal losing the way in political revolution (7)
11 Food in a cup (3)
12 In difficulties because of the squeeze? (4-7)
13 Railway instrument used in a fight (5)
14 Welcomes the sound of something solid in a storm (9)
16 Instruction from Colin — gosh! (9)
17 Put in a scheme to start travelling (5)
19 He has high aspirations (11)
22 Give striking evidence of having been in the sun (3)
23 One may not be welcome to do so (7)
24 One way to move heavily in one's sleep (7)
26 They're given by the man in command (6)
27 Ray giving you a warm smile? (7)

DOWN

1 Saying the expert word (7)
2 He brings the celebrity nominally to book (9, 6)
3 Sources of new life in the Po Valley (3)
4 Will he go out when exhausted? (5)
5 Young streaker? (9)
6 Find a home at the gate, perhaps (5)
7 Figures from time to time from the furniture trade (10, 5)
8 Even a non-drinker may take this (6)
12 Greeting from the depths with a ring (5)
14 His is near to a hirsute change (9)
15 Very good at being an extra actor (5)
16 Top people meet here (6)
18 One isn't pleased to fly into one (7)
20 Peace for a spell — this could be arranged (5)
21 Moves to make more comfortable? (5)
25 Run around a vessel (3)

31

ACROSS

1 Does it prevent one leaving the job? (5, 2, 6)
8 Some of grandmother's lavender water for a foreigner (4)
9 Keep complaining under a rider (3)
10 Please go round and pass by (6)
11 Switched sitters? (10)
13 One front encountered in Russia (4)
14 Humiliate me when the senior man's around (6)
16 Encroached on Peg in dim confusion (8)
19 Contrive to be civil possibly (8)
22 Given a touch of affection (6)
25 Urge to give it to an honoured companion (4)
26 Poised for reform with a politician in store (10)
27 They used to find the place instructive (6)
28 It's refreshing for most of the players (3)
29 One of those things that come at the wrong time (4)
30 Struggle for the bell? (4-4, 5)

DOWN

1 The heat in your food (7)
2 Go ahead with a loan? (7)
3 Three-quarters of the way to old Bob (9)
4 A horn gives warning in it (3)
5 Unpleasant fellow right away from being a pal (5)
6 One hurried ahead of a Scot, being foreign (7)
7 He brings an animal up in oriental employment (7)
12 It's no error to put your foot in it (7)
15 A stick-up, you fool! (3)
17 It's as plain as a fish-pole! (9)
18 Fuel delivery in the main (7)
20 Not at all pleased to be stung (7)
21 Beastly fashionable person? (7)
23 Session on the model's throne? (7)
24 Serious enough to deserve a new set (7)
26 Forgot lines lacking that juicy quality? (5)
28 The fashion of high speed (3)

32

ACROSS

1 Distinction of having the best position in the local? (5, 2, 5)
8 And it can be driven along the line! (4-3)
9 It may be a bore getting this (7)
11 Instrument of importance in the Alps? (10)
12 There's a ban on him keeping other people's money (4)
14 Material given to a worker in the army (8)
16 Savage notes on fire destruction (6)
17 Bring the creature back to be worshipped (3)
19 See what a plain-clothes man may do (6)
21 Turn to men when Mum's around to keep one going (8)
24 Girl right inside for service (4)
25 The sort of passengers British Rail prefer (4-6)
27 Cover return with a girl in a quandary (7)
28 One appreciates having to pay it (7)
29 A chap to cause annoyance with a Christmas gift (12)

DOWN

1 A dog to show the way (7)
2 Cycle men in flurry of bad weather (10)
3 Trumpet, perhaps, making an electrical connection? (8)
4 You've got it coming to you (6)
5 Is it difficult to pluck a true note from? (4)
6 He brings news of our Eric's arrangements (7)
7 Led to expect an estate in the Middle East? (8, 4)
10 Man with cosh embracing his victim in the confusion? (6-6)
13 It sets one free to show hesitation in drink (10)
15 Musician's absconding off-spring (3)
18 Servant in the home (8)
20 Performer who can hold his drink? (7)
22 Platform for the people's defender (7)
23 Mother lays down the code to one in Africa (6)
26 Ring people for an indication of what's to happen (4)

33

ACROSS

6 Difficult problem of applying pressure to obtain a little food (4, 3, 2, 5)
9 No port is passed round so quickly (6)
10 Food cover for a bird (8)
11 The university chap just isn't practical (8)
13 One goes on drawing it all one's life (6)
15 Show girl about to be incorporated shortly (6)
17 Sign of a precious stone in one (6)
19 The father is a holy man or priest (6)
20 Perform acts ripe for reform (8)
22 Waylay a servant and there could be a strike! (8)
24 Late summer character (6)
26 When it's robbery perhaps to make you pay so much? (8, 6)

DOWN

1 Man who played M in the film, for instance? (9, 5)
2 Annoyance at missing tea? Just smile (4)
3 Doing one's best to tell (6)
4 Drink that can be carried? (8)
5 Part of a really nice room (4)
7 A couple of cards in hand (6)
8 There may be agitation in it before one gets a drink (8, 6)
12 Meaning to be carried on the tide (5)
14 Order to prepare to publish about a hundred (5)
16 Drawing them doesn't give you a good view (8)
18 Ask for a second hearing (6)
21 Come down for a match (6)
23 Beast turning up with a master (4)
25 One can't see much in it (4)

34

ACROSS

1 Give one of those lost pauses (8)
5 The university is all round here (6)
9 Skirts an attempt to find a place in Whitehall (8)
10 Fabulous bird to ring a firm in style (6)
12 Oriental study of early horticulture (4)
13 Met acid men concocting a cure (10)
15 Fancy dress hired for a time? (6, 7)
19 Where marksmanship might attain its peak? (8, 5)
23 Row during a speech at a ceremony (10)
25 Mark the way for the vehicle to follow (4)
28 Shiver of excitement (6)
29 Abandoned the German and Spanish before I got caught (8)
30 Some nonsense about a lair for an animal (6)
31 They may be raised in a surprise move (8)

DOWN

1 Get in the way of the food? (6)
2 Give voice to a hot note (5)
3 Try the river (4)
4 Tube traveller heading for a blow-up (7)
6 Perfume of a broken-off romance (5)
7 Proper carry-on (9)
8 Cricketer of uncertain standing? (5, 3)
11 Revolutionary source of music (4)
14 Summons one doesn't quite commit to paper (4)
15 Run and peddle mixture obtained illegally (9)
16 Put on as a teacher (3)
17 Go down in the kitchen (4)
18 He adds to our foreign exchange problems (8)
20 Spot one on the roundabout with thanks (4)
21 Evil resort of birds (7)
22 Noble Roman killer (6)
24 Is a leg in it any longer? (5)
26 Atmosphere in a business providing capital (5)
27 That girl Bridget's first letter may be a plant (4)

35

ACROSS

1 Use influence to tighten the knot? (4, 7)
9 Lavish public relations having some value (7)
10 Agony applying to people in the right (7)
11 He'll be crazy in a minute! (3)
12 A span cut short (7)
13 Finish the bottle and turn up late to show rank (7)
14 It all adds up to money (3)
15 He wants to be the first arrival (5)
17 She's quite taken in by the smart champagne set (5)
18 Rapid move to clean up (5)
20 Look threatening and comparatively depressed (5)
22 It shows places where a girl can make a comeback (3)
24 In a novel state in Gaza (7)
25 Fights differential rises on a backstreet (7)
26 Not worth including so few (3)
27 Get in touch with some force (7)
28 Spoil one in the gallery after six (7)
29 Here some blooming hiker got up (7, 4)

DOWN

1 He's paid to let you know what's going to happen (9, 6)
2 Clean up and rule in a new way (7)
3 A row is just part of the act (5)
4 No good taking a line in Hyde Park (6, 3)
5 Ivan ran around in a blissful state (7)
6 Something wrong with the letters you've given (8, 7)
7 Waters the flowers (6)
8 Standing in a rank? (6)
16 As distinct from hot metal bullets (4, 5)
18 Power of personal communication (6)
19 Bond's extra payment (7)
21 Its root may provide something to eat (7)
23 Person sending letters for publicity purposes? (6)
25 He gets around, the dog! (5)

36

ACROSS

1 Got to a point of discomfort in debt (7)
5 You've done well to earn it! (6)
9 State of grace (7)
10 It doesn't allow one to move after the amber changes (7)
11 Tea taken repeatedly during a dance (3)
12 Result of a message putting the needle-in? (5-6)
13 Get stuck among Masons? (5)
14 Supplied fish under a new arrangement (9)
16 Wasn't in a hurry to make progress (9)
17 Exciting movement to get out of a bathrobe (5)
19 He can't wait to get a word in! (11)
22 Possibly electric provider of current movement (3)
23 Country people in song (7)
24 Where an egg may be an oyster? (7)
26 Effect of an economic blizzard on wages (6)
27 Regret about dashing off a dotty message (7)

DOWN

1 Car dial showing quite a marked change (7)
2 Troublesome client for the charm school? (7, 8)
3 Burden of bricklayer's mate (3)
4 Break up the crowd of soldiers shortly? (5)
5 Shares one would rather have (9)
6 Scope for a piece before lunch (5)
7 One may be prone to be carried away by him (9-6)
8 Given striking evidence that the girl is in fish (6)
12 There may be treasure in it on the personal front (5)
14 Fun to tear around if you're lucky! (9)
15 Put into digs for a permanent stay? (5)
16 Going around giving a rise (6)
18 Accept from the teller (7)
20 Mountains in cattle country? (5)
21 He needs a lot of drink to be the man he is (5)
25 It may be taken with striking intent (3)

37

ACROSS

1 Drink from the wine snob? (6-7)
8 Netted in some shape (4)
9 Go round to drink (3)
10 His rag is given a showy display (6)
11 Nasty to upset the prince with proof of his debts! (10)
13 Man most likely to succeed (4)
14 Be a heavenly creature and start again, girl! (6)
16 Going on doing a nude turn before a call (8)
19 Threatening trouble on the left (8)
22 Gives protection in the depression (6)
25 Guns for a mail vessel (4)
26 First Ernie must bring about a revolution in France (10)
27 Quite a few pints of bitter taken on (6)
28 Half chance of some refreshment (3)
29 Move towards the revolutionary heaven (4)
30 Product of instant politics that can be entertaining? (8, 5)

DOWN

1 That woman called to show where liquor's to be had? (7)
2 Intensify the confusion of a bird by breaking a cane (7)
3 Dramatically loth to be peer or debutante (9)
4 Tea for the winner? (3)
5 Go up in a vehicle that's deceptive (5)
6 Not a dog for steady companionship? (7)
7 Foreigner encountered in one's salad days? (7)
12 Go too far too fast? (7)
15 May go off and kill someone (3)
17 Gives an impression of the occasion (4, 5)
18 Man of some brilliance (3)
20 Are they made for the attackers' transport? (7)
21 Like the Corsicans or the Irish, for instance? (7)
23 Oriental clergyman sets things up (7)
24 Hasty shout about ours being in trouble (7)
26 One who imposes penalties on the more admirable? (5)
28 Island belonging to the firm (3)

38

ACROSS

1 He may get an award for a striking performance (5-7)
8 There used to be quite enough for instance (7)
9 Struck down and put into a depression? (4, 3)
11 The dentist's ancestry? (10)
12 Like turning it into wine (4)
14 Male looking at two ducks in the bird world (8)
16 Upset an arrangement overhead (6)
17 Be quick to cause pain (3)
19 Rolling stone? (6)
21 Aspiration to win the booby prize? (4, 4)
24 He's been fooled! (4)
25 Unable to make sense of the nice Ron (10)
27 A letter reveals his status (7)
28 In time a girl looks quite ordinary (7)
29 Striking product of the Wimbledon Mafia? (6-6)

DOWN

1 Can be moulded finally into a small picture (7)
2 Not to be appeased by one movement of the palm
and a message (10)
3 Chance to give cross approval (8)
4 Ten slog around constructing dwellings (6)
5 Greet in a cold shower (4)
6 Takes a service engagement (7)
7 Award for putting up a fight (7, 5)
10 Colourless girl bringing luck to the Scots? (5, 7)
13 Jam making it difficult to get at the drink? (6-4)
15 Olive's essential extraction (3)
18 View of a girl between her parents (8)
20 Put back material with some ornamentation (7)
22 Go in for too much drama? (7)
23 Producer of pictures partly being restored (6)
26 Soon a girl will have nothing inside (4)

39

ACROSS

6 They may enclose examples of literary talk (8, 6)
9 Opening blow bringing a cry of pain (6)
10 Spin out in an expert pamphlet (8)
11 Walks into a mess (8)
13 Take on quite an amount in a rough sea (6)
15 Being observant or getting the sack, one takes it (6)
17 Refusal to admit doing an idle turn (6)
19 Go along the road with some bread (6)
20 Bring back skill so that poetry can get across (8)
22 Force exerted by the customer? (8)
24 Take out of the underground (6)
26 Some dishonesty is being cooked up here! (7, 7)

DOWN

1 Final request for a loan added for perfection? (9, 5)
2 Eager to see a singer arise (4)
3 The archaeologist may have it in hand (6)
4 A touch of distinction (8)
5 Old poet nothing can spoil (4)
7 Treat in a revealing way (6)
8 Social skill required to get something done (14)
12 It's often said to mean a lot to a man (5)
14 Get along with notably little friction (5)
16 Got together after a time in poor weather (8)
18 Take off and move in line? (6)
21 Wards off a vaster upheaval (6)
23 Man responsible for some French effects in the kitchen (4)
25 A couple of laughs in the depression (2-2)

40

ACROSS

1 Very good at frightening people? (8)
5 Evangelist and Roman in a place of business (6)
9 Reduce to eliminate the crumpled look? (8)
10 Award expected for one of the palace maids? (6)
12 Is he entitled to be drunk? (4)
13 Large scent distribution in certain areas (10)
15 The sense not to be naive? (7, 6)
19 It's found not to belong to anyone (8, 5)
23 Acquittal may be the answer to Jack (10)
25 Covering a province in Africa (4)
28 Game to make a complaint (6)
29 There's little time to run for him (8)
30 Time one has another one (6)
31 Manufacturer in favour of crude alterations (8)

DOWN

1 Go along on your own and get led astray (6)
2 Repeatedly refer to the dog (5)
3 It may be thought of as a bit of road-side art (4)
4 Sent Ida round as substitute (7)
6 A firm linked with the Navy has big growth potential (5)
7 Week-long turn round duke's head for enlightenment (9)
8 Annoying occasion when Rose takes a break inside (8)
11 Visit the way it's agreed (4)
14 Eye a girl? (4)
15 It gives the swordsman the edge (9)
16 Deceptive position (3)
17 Put the pressure on with smooth effect (4)
18 Get to grips with fatality (8)
20 One's name occasionally comes round on it (4)
21 Like him, one could swear! (7)
22 The burden's on him to hold an artist up in the drink (6)
24 Ellis about to give us a yarn (5)
26 Like a worker providing some fun? (5)
27 Not at all pleased to be outside civilisation (4)

41

ACROSS

1 Indulge in wild talk to relieve the pressure (3, 3, 5)
9 Where schooner had wheels (7)
10 Point of attack (7)
11 Beast of a vessel (3)
12 Monument where the bloke is taking a break (7)
13 Makes a coat easier to put on (7)
14 It's up at 100 m.p.h. (3)
15 His murder caused dismay among fliers (5)
17 Not a very cheerful fate coming back and giving you a start (5)
18 One may have this alternative (5)
20 Very good at describing Britain (5)
22 Unhappy one leaving an Egyptian port (3)
24 Staff pet is rather a stinker! (7)
25 Ray is kept off by a girl's defence (7)
26 Strip quietly off to become a swimmer (3)
27 On which one seems to have got somewhere (7)
28 An old lady with energy causing surprise (7)
29 Where space travellers can reap some benefit? (7, 4)

DOWN

1 Abandon a companion and get away when there's a sudden movement (5, 2, 3, 5)
2 Barker from Aberdeen or Manchester, maybe (7)
3 By no means an ordinary, straightforward faker (5)
4 Matter of taking a lower position (9)
5 Great place for an old Greek to be seen dead in (7)
6 He has most of the law, it's said (3, 2, 10)
7 Grow up fast in Brussels? (6)
8 Weather for an old song (6)
16 Game for some light music? (9)
18 Waif found at a public house in an Algerian town (6)
19 Rescue and give new protection (7)
21 Damaged with some stir in a storm (7)
23 Pull into the river when there's a flood (6)
25 Put down in the factory (5)

42

ACROSS

1 Sleep hath dissolved in oil (7)
5 Turn in and shove around to chastise (6)
9 Some small measure of conscience? (7)
10 Having corners where there should be curves (7)
11 Flier for a spell? (3)
12 There are certain things they know about (11)
13 Morning dress? (3-2)
14 Good quality of hi-fi equipment? (9)
16 Change a net wrongly every second (9)
17 I would take man initially, in a manner of speaking (5)
19 Set a limit to one's work as an artist? (4, 3, 4)
22 Money a sailor has in a rag (3)
23 Wearisome complaints in a stable relationship? (7)
24 He doesn't know it all yet (7)
26 Amount in credit when there's a depression (6)
27 Don't go on about the pleasure (7)

DOWN

1 Began so badly to provide a food holder (7)
2 Without fault? You don't know him! (7, 8)
3 Incline to show appreciation (3)
4 Lead astray on the way to see a girl (5)
5 It's ordinarily said to show quiet scope (9)
6 He needs support in getting up (5)
7 Quality of the reluctant customer (5, 10)
8 Credit is repeatedly required at the decisive moment (6)
12 Very good and maybe better! (5)
14 With a little knowledge a man seeking retribution can be cleaner (9)
15 Hit up to the house? (5)
16 Putting something on (6)
18 High point of eastern worship (7)
20 More demanding revolutionary character? (5)
21 Riled when ruffled but he won't do anything (5)
25 Are you singular in skill? (3)

43

ACROSS

1 Gain a lot by striking the sailor amidships? (3, 3, 7)
8 First person to cause an obstruction (4)
9 A gift for the speaker (3)
10 Beast of a diversion in Milan! (6)
11 On the beat with the Irishman showing he's had a few (10)
13 Enthusiast for streaking? (4)
14 Implore Alf to come back inside and do the decorating (6)
16 What one shows here is impressive (8)
19 Authorises a chap to make appointments (8)
22 Is Adam's boy a girl? (6)
25 He produces food in such effortless ways! (4)
26 The divinity of Rhode Island? (10)
27 One may appear in a jacket at dinner (6)
28 Seed for some sort of hen? (3)
29 Act on directions in Ireland (4)
30 Missing only one occasion on alternate dates? (5, 5, 3)

DOWN

1 Compound containing water from the yard (7)
2 Revolutionary transport (7)
3 Outstanding feature of superior brilliance (9)
4 Work for man with afflictions (3)
5 Sound of something dropped in error (5)
6 Wrestling with an ape Bill can easily be bent (7)
7 The business of the streets (7)
12 That's laying it on a bit thick! (7)
15 Enthusiast giving himself airs? (3)
17 Get rid of a line time switch (9)
18 Raise prohibition to make a catch (3)
20 Halt when there's trouble over one in Ireland (7)
21 Fed up with being unpunctual to take the air (7)
23 I'm finished being given change (7)
24 Bet on the horse coming back again? (4, 3)
26 Blooming note swallowed by an animal! (5)
28 Animal to whip if it's a dog (3)

44

ACROSS

1 Spirited bravery of some foreign people? (5, 7)
8 Very happy to be giving out heat? (7)
9 Falls into an understanding? (7)
11 A caustic 'No' shows this charge is misplaced (10)
12 In truth she goes to town! (4)
14 The Saint doesn't appear too confident here (8)
16 Daring neckline seen in a dive? (6)
17 Note in which money is mentioned (3)
19 Bible man taking the first one back for a wash (6)
21 Look again in the hope of making a discovery (8)
24 It's up for a splendid meal! (4)
25 After the talk he hopes to get a bargain (10)
27 Called with nothing on out east (7)
28 He won't appreciate being put in the fire! (7)
29 No doubt the best are first to get this award (5, 2, 5)

DOWN

1 Takes away the channels? (7)
2 There may be strain on it in getting across (10)
3 Covering defence may be a hanging matter (8)
4 Ring and put the point badly for choice (6)
5 More than a day's work for the builder (4)
6 Female with a fellow in a ship (7)
7 Green for danger, blow it! (12)
10 He gets a friendly response from the venomous (5-7)
13 Giving out notes seems fun for him (4-6)
15 High point observable to the right (3)
18 It's good to enjoy yourself in ethical doctrine (8)
20 He'll instruct you along certain lines, no doubt (7)
22 Take back what's been said about the land (7)
23 Building requiring support (4-2)
26 Deal with the problem of what a priest might wear (4)

45

ACROSS

6 Do they shelter those who have come over the sea to them? (7, 7)
9 Rascal one found in a restaurant possibly (6)
10 Abandoned ship (8)
11 As elegant as a princess (8)
13 Style of horror writing? (6)
15 Risk the unexpected (6)
17 Gentlemen of the old school (6)
19 Deal with an obstruction in a boring way (6)
20 A legislator eager to alter the current amount (8)
22 Something as colourful as a running cold? (8)
24 Substance for one taking paper for brass? (6)
26 Make a final appearance holding a train? (5, 2, 3, 4)

DOWN

1 On which one might give a shocking performance? (8, 6)
2 Drink to a number in the group (4)
3 Charges Jack if heading the field (6)
4 Moulding silver into starry form (8)
5 Send after it on Tyneside (4)
7 Cheat prepared to be misled (6)
8 During which the elderly have to say no? (9, 5)
12 Something rather restrictive to take tea in (5)
14 Devon and Cornwall division (5)
16 Most of the troops got transport, he discovered (8)
18 Knock up some nonsense that might be repetitive (6)
21 He is able to carry drink (6)
23 Flier from Inverness (4)
25 If small it's unimportant (4)

46

ACROSS

1 High point of land reclamation? (4-4)
5 Puts back primitive instincts that don't make sense (6)
9 Not quite certain to find a horse to get on (8)
10 Give Martin a turn in Ireland (6)
12 Bear losing its head in a whirl (4)
13 Is father's new lady a dancer? (10)
15 He has his place among people of substance (8, 5)
19 Rubbish is his business (3-3-4-3)
23 Not yet the perfect professional in action? (10)
25 Result of taking superficial measures (4)
28 Make a permanent home up north (6)
29 Holy footballer we haven't met (8)
30 Egg production agreed in fishy surroundings (6)
31 Scattered when the raid went wrong and the cops came back round (8)

DOWN

1 She may be relatively religious (6)
2 Biting one in a card shuffle (5)
3 It's set in motion by a young bowler (4)
4 She finds an obstruction in the stake money (7)
6 Tag on and move round in a dance (5)
7 Bit a bird on the temple (9)
8 Sugar from a dreamer (8)
11 See the point (4)
14 Spend very little time on the space traveller's objective (4)
15 Show time in the food store (9)
16 Port where girl lost her man (3)
17 No stamp needed for resistance units (4)
18 Engaging suggestion (8)
20 A second letter to invite us to lie (4)
21 Making an interminable carry-on (7)
22 Has the making of a material (6)
24 Hook carrying a pound in weight (5)
26 In a very shaken condition (5)
27 Just light-headed? (4)

47

ACROSS

1 Some sort of pressure to rewrite this car poem (11)
9 He provides food for a pet with some hesitations (7)
10 Brave workers providing a bitter following (7)
11 Tree down in the forest (3)
12 Moving like a mischief-maker in the heather (7)
13 Is he too trendy to use the roundabouts? (7)
14 Ready for some shooting? (3)
15 Possession of the filthy rich? (5)
17 Power accompaniment (5)
18 Bird boot (5)
20 After half a century the advantage is outstanding (5)
22 Look around the cathedral? (3)
24 Takes it easy where the drinking's done (7)
25 Here to make an introduction (7)
26 Fowl food? (3)
27 Idle Tom worried by that dated look (3-4)
28 Biting someone wordily witty (7)
29 A collection of clockwork soldiers? (7, 4)

DOWN

1 Accusation that one tried to kill? (9, 6)
2 Fighting Roman poet? (7)
3 End of the neck (5)
4 Quick to get topped up on drugs (4-5)
5 Moving like a musical stone? (7)
6 It may give players a different background (6, 2, 7)
7 They give a man pull in a vessel (6)
8 Try some endless changes that can be violent (6)
16 Letters of ice, for instance? (4, 5)
18 Pattern of weeping? (6)
19 Tackle a swindling arrangement (7)
21 You can distinguish her from the real one (7)
23 Being one that has reality (6)
25 Copy in public relations journal (5)

48

ACROSS

1 Buoyant advice to end smoking? (4, 3)
5 Insult as being unimportant? (6)
9 A warily arranged travel facility (7)
10 Impress most of the men as being serious (7)
11 Animal like a snake at first (3)
12 Prompt in organising a journey? (11)
13 Rising out of the return of a twelve-gallon keg (5)
14 University official taking in one of the Lawrences as guardian (9)
16 Ned panted around as a hanger-on (9)
17 Wonderful description of Britain! (5)
19 Signs of mobility in a stoic Indian (11)
22 Number of an unidentified person (3)
23 Gifts of ancient money (7)
24 Goes around the bend (7)
26 Proverbial form of reproach (6)
27 Pippin's bones carry weight (7)

DOWN

1 Where the driver becomes a pedestrian (3, 4)
2 A fall brought matters to a dramatic halt? (4, 7, 4)
3 Pull in direction of America (3)
4 Give money to a superior? (3, 2)
5 It moves fast to beat dopes to the turn (5-4)
6 Bar obtained after getting in (5)
7 Instant flare-up of anger? (4, 2, 3, 6)
8 Possibly a forbidding filmgoer (6)
12 She has a part in an excellent production (5)
14 Experienced as a doctor? (9)
15 Moves slowly round the outside? (5)
16 Brief interval in time for something tasteful (6)
18 One star turn sure to earn royal disapproval (7)
20 Inability to describe a revolution in verse (5)
21 Happen to bring the business up before the dog (5)
25 The snag about acquiring polish? (3)

49

ACROSS

1 By which progress is made when seizures begin? (4, 3, 6)
8 Fruit a German brought back (4)
9 Appreciate how to get beneath the surface (3)
10 He hopes to make an unofficial currency transfer (6)
11 Very angry or very loving (10)
13 One body that's part of the community (4)
14 Time to display spirit (6)
16 Plaything of the little girl in cute nightwear? (4, 4)
19 Cheerful society girl doing a broadcast (8)
22 Vehicle carrying the weight of a box (6)
25 Perhaps Edward can show you part of the church (4)
26 A man is able to identify a monk (10)
27 Go off to put things right (6)
28 Silver ring in the past (3)
29 Press club? (4)
30 Lover's messages conveyed by empty sugar bags? (5, 8)

DOWN

1 One day opening a ship (7)
2 East End motive for crime (7)
3 Dead Roman reformed in heaven (9)
4 Follow in a pet? (3)
5 The crowd beyond the company (5)
6 Come back to be given new cover (7)
7 Unusual formation of ice in the Alps (7)
12 Man starting again in Canada (7)
15 A pound in a garment (3)
17 It helps to put an actor in the picture (9)
18 Not among those present (3)
20 Quick to get out of newspapers (7)
21 Work in a theatre (7)
23 In a hurry, it could be said, to become European, perhaps (7)
24 They're great talkers (7)
26 Number one Wood Street (5)
28 A party commotion (3)

50

ACROSS

1 So very unaffected it's miraculous! (12)
8 He hasn't a true wife (7)
9 Find to be out of this world? (7)
11 Started to turn into a dirge (10)
12 A medal given to him would be a big one (4)
14 Knight using a soldier's weapon a great deal (8)
16 City information girl (6)
17 Service provided by some of the craftsmen (3)
19 Cap set to give an appearance (6)
21 Given striking evidence of hostility (8)
24 Walk back from a Pinkerton encounter (4)
25 He has some chance of success with gold (10)
27 Complaining about the protection provided (7)
28 Scene of dramatic operations (7)
29 Time taken to complete the cycle (6, 6)

DOWN

1 Cutting a portion (7)
2 One gains it by outstanding achievement (10)
3 Warming manifestation of radio art (8)
4 Crazy dame around us when we entertained (6)
5 In no condition for a new sale (4)
6 Inflationary aid to personal mobility? (3, 4)
7 He may appear as Homer to class (12)
10 Great Dane to amuse the children (4, 8)
13 Payment into the sinking fund? (10)
15 Upside down creature in check (3)
18 Unnaturally high because of the wrong drink mixture (8)
20 Chance for a quiet survey before the opening (7)
22 Goes round to stare improperly (7)
23 Accent on the foot (6)
26 Its run is quite ordinary (4)

51

ACROSS

6 Jumpy means by which to get ahead (5, 3, 6)
9 Game between the banks (6)
10 Going straight after getting in some roundabout way (8)
11 Neat maid made to look lively (8)
13 Take the cover off (6)
15 Chap in time to see what's wrong (6)
17 Effort to show breeding? (6)
19 Rose is given a turn by the basket-makers (6)
20 Reject a TV throw-away line? (3, 5)
22 Mob Anita roughly in Canada (8)
24 He comes in old-fashioned style to the theatre (6)
26 Get a rise after a successful take-off (6-8)

DOWN

1 The error of looking hostile? (7, 7)
2 All-round players? (4)
3 Agreement in the form of a dispatch (6)
4 Tie on bed to make amenable (8)
5 Sound content with one of several lives (4)
7 Chap turning up with announcements for the nymphs (6)
8 Birds in a water skipping game (5, 3, 6)
12 Give me shelter in a fight (5)
14 Series of ringing laughs? (5)
16 Find how to reform Rod's vice (8)
18 Invite Bible teacher to appear as an African soldier (6)
21 Novel hat girl? (6)
23 Being much admired, I perform with a learner (4)
25 Is he belted for being so superior? (4)

52

ACROSS

1 By strength of necessity (8)
5 Say what you like, it's free! (6)
9 Is it applied for camouflage purposes? (3, 5)
10 An old copper is quiet before the Spanish drive away (6)
12 She's back in the ballet (4)
13 Relative security? (10)
15 Acts as go-between for those who are not extreme (13)
19 They show things aren't quite right (13)
23 The full dig can be very pleasant (10)
25 Face one in bringing the boy back (4)
28 Man from the East finding a boy for a girl (6)
29 Smoke many put down to cause whiteness (8)
30 Point of entry into the joint (6)
31 Headline in coloured paper? (8)

DOWN

1 Does it give a girl explosive make-up? (6)
2 The way life is out of town (5)
3 Stone from a ring given to a friend (4)
4 Study the route as a line on the map (7)
6 Indicate the sharp end (5)
7 Thus a peer may be thrown into the river (9)
8 The man's about to have a bad spell when he can't move (8)
11 Spend in colourful style (4)
14 One having all-round points as a performer (4)
15 Not having thought to take such action (9)
16 Scot giving protection (3)
17 It's hard to achieve a smooth effect (4)
18 Blow over a girl in a revolutionary pull-up (8)
20 Takes consumer action (4)
21 He gets around (7)
22 It isn't sporting of him to make notes (6)
24 Layer of foolishness? (5)
26 One striking manifestation of religion (5)
27 Carrier of drinks in the beer-cellar (4)

53

ACROSS

1 Digger of the highest skill as pack leader? (3, 2, 6)
9 Like an animal or one of the Popes (7)
10 Land in the water? (7)
11 Just the little chap to get in! (3)
12 It may be made to transfer money (7)
13 At last a creditor and provided with money! (7)
14 Self discovery in some good works (3)
15 Little creatures one approves? (5)
17 Not entirely due to a pet providing the gold (5)
18 The energy to follow Augustus shortly (5)
20 Revolutionary acts (5)
22 War leader's bad end (3)
24 Most superior working gear (7)
25 It's all one to the Scot if the girl comes back (7)
26 Night hooter (3)
27 Room to be painted? (7)
28 Tin seen to collapse under strain (7)
29 Are energetic athletes full of them? (6-5)

DOWN

1 One doesn't make a name writing it (9, 6)
2 Well known to be of superior height (7)
3 Quick to provide the craft (5)
4 University man bringing new order to poor serfs (9)
5 Dead Red knocked about a bit, it's feared (7)
6 Landfall for a snack (8, 7)
7 Pass one way by mistake (6)
8 Outlaw the group providing it (6)
16 Possible purchases may be mentioned in it (9)
18 Game to make a complaint? (6)
19 Appreciation shown with eggs? (7)
21 Island fund over at the Royal Academy (7)
23 The one in front (6)
25 Take exercise and become elevated (5)

54

ACROSS

1 Put down from topside (7)
5 Mineral in large bottles, we hear (6)
9 Carrier on the beach to give protection? (7)
10 Pacify an animal that's swallowed some vegetables (7)
11 Doctor novel ending in the past (3)
12 No doubt his Lordship has a right to it (11)
13 Aspect of a point in truth (5)
14 Made haste after achieving a security muddle (9)
16 Study of 'What's My Line'? (9)
17 Kenneth Robinson's inner rhythm (5)
19 Parrot with views as to what we all think? (7, 4)
22 Cat to start mousing (3)
23 One might have a shot at squeezing it (7)
24 Takes a chance on breaking Mab's leg (7)
26 Sick of plumbing the United Nation's depths? (6)
27 Retribution in oriental mess, perhaps (7)

DOWN

1 Perhaps fads fit for the female side (7)
2 One is ruddy well in it! (4, 2, 9)
3 Cry out in flagrant disobedience (3)
4 Too mean to have been drinking (5)
5 Rely for a change on a bottle from time to time (9)
6 For the teacher from Paris? (5)
7 Such as one might read in a railway magazine? (10, 5)
8 Like one's interest in keeping warm, for instance? (6)
12 Ten in a different rate yields more (5)
14 Wrong run closed by a crook (9)
15 Very little time to phone for accommodation (5)
16 It may give one higher standing (6)
18 Money raised among suckers causes confusion (7)
20 Fire one when old Bob's gone (5)
21 No rag arrangement for an instrument (5)
25 Not saying one is the parent (3)

55

ACROSS

1 There's no job that girl can't do! (4, 2, 3, 4)
8 To tell the truth, blow it, it's nonsense! (4)
9 Bring me back about a pound of wood (3)
10 It's expected at a popular opening (6)
11 Her fingers are crooked in an invigorating way (10)
13 Foreign money man (4)
14 Powerful and obstinate with the head (6)
16 No points to be won for being civil (8)
19 Gone to find something to play in the act (8)
22 One sergeant-major in a day can cause consternation (6)
25 Stone work making Alice lose her cool (4)
26 Anxiety of family lawyer? (10)
27 Distant association? (6)
28 Creature in a delicate condition (3)
29 Thick ear (4)
30 Spender can have fun on it (8, 5)

DOWN

1 Give me a home of minimum pretension (7)
2 Deduce disagreement from all that heat! (7)
3 The supervisor's error? (9)
4 Intention to have one in the morning (3)
5 Prone to be deceptive (5)
6 Having a row makes him what he is (7)
7 Flier finding a good man right in the bottom of the boat (7)
12 He doesn't believe in a revolutionary ruler (7)
15 Blame for a knock (3)
17 Puts one's finger on a faulty act inside (9)
18 Crazy get-up causes hold-up (3)
20 Train to put into words (7)
21 All over spilt gore with brisk movement (7)
23 He'll pay his debts and make a home (7)
24 You can hear how blue Ida might be (7)
26 Gone up sharply in price (5)
28 Able to take Ada to another country (3)

56

ACROSS

1 Cite a captain in order to disable (12)
8 He used to be an outsider (7)
9 Is the revised claim of religious significance? (7)
11 Directing a vessel sailing erratically (10)
12 Spend very little time on a satellite (4)
14 Does he publicise his practice? (8)
16 What's the matter? A very loud tune! (6)
17 Go down for a bathe (3)
19 Not the feeling of a friend (6)
21 Scots crying to new arrivals? (8)
24 A worker who has the touch? (4)
25 Diplomat Brown starts to be a specialist (10)
27 After a drink one needs a small column (7)
28 House no man is able to build (7)
29 Different densities to test the faithful sticker (5, 3, 4)

DOWN

1 Rouse with something burning (7)
2 Get involved in making things difficult (10)
3 Fairy took off and died (8)
4 He makes work for a professional (6)
5 It holds cash up to a point (4)
6 Man taking up a high ball for the prize-giving (7)
7 It made a man one of the earliest Christians (12)
10 Getting together in church? (12)
13 Time for a digest (5, 5)
15 Outfit for doing some drilling? (3)
18 Took for granted there might be a mud spree (8)
20 Top person getting on in a demonstration (7)
22 The language of the fellow in Rome! (7)
23 Flora's ring (6)
26 Last letter incorporated at first in metal (4)

57

ACROSS

6 Play host at the launching? (4, 3, 4, 3)
9 Rumour of a quarrel? (6)
10 A red seen to compose music (8)
11 That heel could be a killer! (8)
13 Send away right after shifting the dope (6)
15 Put it back in the middle of the day — that's the idea (6)
17 All right in a gun that's out of order (6)
19 Laurel taking notes of the position (6)
20 Plant the French husband in a job (8)
22 It gets in the way during a race (8)
24 Finished work is not to be expected from such hooligans (6)
26 Such as Solomon might have given the Queen of Sheba? (6, 2, 6)

DOWN

1 It offers a basis for a personal carve-up (9, 5)
2 Fair, perhaps, for a sweater (4)
3 The way of the ordinary man (6)
4 One of the internal ways of power? (8)
5 Give striking cause for astonishment (4)
7 End of the line for Scotsmen (6)
8 Dominated by digital pressure (5, 4, 5)
12 Bad language applied to the dog (5)
14 Game to get stuck into heating (5)
16 Dominating actors on a dull day? (8)
18 The very thing! (6)
21 Late summer saint (6)
23 No red is to shorten the railway (4)
25 Cancel the performance (4)

58

ACROSS

1 Roma's fee makes a frightful change (8)
5 Eggs returned after a month according to size (6)
9 Behaving badly, say, going to the city? Shows you're sick (8)
10 Strength of sea creature, so one hears (6)
12 The way to see the rising (4)
13 Pushed in to do some modelling between times? (10)
15 Invitation to observe the speedy movement of a trio lacking vision (3, 3, 4, 3)
19 Happening as a result of one quiet clan's dispersal (13)
23 Stanley's old home (10)
25 What a business with mother in a trance! (4)
28 Striking personality (6)
29 Nice sea movement in the works (8)
30 Lives at end of Llandrindo (6)
31 Change your seat and there's a chance of seeing a star (8)

DOWN

1 Hurry and tie up? (6)
2 Champagne set girl (5)
3 Low fellow with an almost new turn-up (4)
4 Find me chaps to provide a keep-sake (7)
6 Some sort of chop, you fool! (5)
7 Sent Clara round from our fathers (9)
8 Exhausted by too much cooking? (8)
11 Inclination to be crooked (4)
14 Where Willie's head is lost (4)
15 Daisy's machine — or the airs she gave herself? (4-5)
16 We have taken in nothing but sorrow (3)
17 Animated rising isn't good! (4)
18 Fought to get thrown away (8)
20 Impulse to incite? (4)
21 Old ones not quite right in the head? (7)
22 Impediment to knighthood for composer (6)
24 Right for one bit of business (5)
26 All right to give father a turn with one animal (5)
27 Point of personal protection (4)

59

ACROSS

1 Jack getting involved with a tie, perhaps (7, 4)
9 Raise in a superior way (7)
10 Having inclinations to be awkward? (7)
11 Have a session on the bench (3)
12 Policeman taking an Indian's money in the wood (7)
13 Cheer up the archdeacon after taking the wrong line (7)
14 One of a number of women under discipline (3)
15 High-minded toff starting to leave (5)
17 Not so if it's any good! (5)
18 One last letter to that rotter in Spain! (5)
20 Not the circle for insiders (5)
22 Part of the Colditz series seen before? (3)
24 Itch to find a way to take a letter from the taxi drivers (7)
25 High-class girl needing a boy, it's argued (7)
26 Colour with a cry (3)
27 It's a drag to take it with you (7)
28 Story of how the lawyers got back within the enclosure (7)
29 Union pair who never agree (3, 2, 1, 5)

DOWN

1 Drink to lay you out cold in bed? (8-7)
2 Spike turns up at one looking foreign (7)
3 Honour on the Stock Exchange carrying a lot of weight (5)
4 Tent-mates upset by something that's said (9)
5 Criticised in trifling detail (7)
6 Supporter of popular entertainment (10, 5)
7 Signal that it might be a trick (6)
8 One gets very excited in it (6)
16 Much erudition may rest on it (9)
18 Exchange chessmen in defence (6)
19 Doctor brought to book (7)
21 She could easily become an art bore (7)
23 Artful Dickensian (6)
25 Drank up in the warehouse (5)

60

ACROSS

1 Happy Diana is wrong but she's in the right! (7)
5 One does well to earn it (6)
9 Colour of a sort of shirt given to farm workers (7)
10 Edinburgh's men in the street? (7)
11 Go downhill like a sportsman (3)
12 What follows is of some importance (11)
13 For instance, meat is to be found in Surrey (5)
14 One isn't prepared to have to do so (9)
16 The racing game? (9)
17 Just the place for the plaster saint (5)
19 To put people off I make a speech that will get worse (11)
22 It may give one standing at the door (3)
23 Group about to end life in the kitchen (7)
24 Go around showing affection (7)
26 Wood and iron from a ship (6)
27 Shorten a span (7)

DOWN

1 One poster could provide the answer (7)
2 More than usually waggish creature when happy (3, 4, 3, 5)
3 Copy a Gibraltar resident (3)
4 Brown follows it up in a big way (5)
5 Shoot holes in a vessel to add spice to a meal (6-3)
6 It's goodbye to Paris (5)
7 Moment of domination by a deputy? (6, 2, 7)
8 Sectarian Jew in German town beginning again (6)
12 It gives the reader pause (5)
14 In which a writer might take a dip (3-6)
15 One animal in a pound (5)
16 He has nothing on for the time being (6)
18 It's as far as one can go (7)
20 He can provide bread, nothing more (5)
21 Artist turning up with a girl where there may be a fight (5)
25 Keep out the lawyers! (3)

61

ACROSS

1 Girls providing the cheese-cake at court? (5, 2, 6)
8 Flag within vision (4)
9 Venomous part of a speaker's tirade (3)
10 Sound move that is plainly Russian (6)
11 They may be deceptive in an original way (10)
13 Show sense in refusing to go to America (4)
14 Case on one side of the depression (6)
16 Last piece of journalism in the book? (8)
19 Left helpless in a London street (8)
22 Drink taken by a Pole in dark surroundings (6)
25 A beginner in a pretty rough trade (4)
26 Is he as smart as Alec? (6, 4)
27 Heard confession on Tuesday? (6)
28 Indelicate person (3)
29 Fiery saint (4)
30 'No thank you' (6, 7)

DOWN

1 Ancient poetic figure (7)
2 Look at different pins, etc. (7)
3 Quite broken up by shifts in the trades (9)
4 He's affected with a passion for dressing up (3)
5 Ring a small relative — it might be refreshing (5)
6 Islands in a lot of water (7)
7 Carrying away in a transport (7)
12 Late coming across with what's expected (7)
15 Radio music? (3)
17 One can't have faith in this (9)
18 Enclosure for a bird (3)
20 Where buying may bring childish delight (7)
21 Give the creature a kiss, duck — that's a great deal at fifty! (7)
23 Where to make a speech? (7)
24 Claimed to make some sort of point (7)
26 Part of the body in a box (5)
28 It may have a mark of reservation (3)

62

ACROSS

1 Eric can trade another way in prison (12)
8 Where gunners grow grapes in the depressions? (7)
9 He expresses contempt in different ways in many offices (4-3)
11 Look after a child satisfactorily in Scotland (10)
12 Woman's dress for a man is such a bore! (4)
14 Team display of minor importance (4-4)
16 Ceased to travel and escaped penalty (3, 3)
17 Give him a ring for going round the wall (3)
19 He was responsible for many inventions noised around (6)
21 Led super detour when thrown back (8)
24 Protection in the post (4)
25 Not having the importance of the cloth? (10)
27 Putting up the wrong air to perform (7)
28 Take out of the land (7)
29 In which a light creature may be described by an admirer? (7, 5)

DOWN

1 Asked in at six with a man (7)
2 Misappropriation by a missionary? (10)
3 Girl courted for making fine furniture (8)
4 Throws out when cross in disturbed sleep (6)
5 A victorious start on the river (4)
6 Stop but move after the amber changes (7)
7 Does it not carry the smarter sort of passenger? (5, 7)
10 Good sound quality (4, 8)
13 Many take employment and tear around but not he! (5-5)
15 Trouble a game chap may have at the den (3)
18 Rotten impression made after taking a month over a letter (8)
20 Just a start when one's making one's name (7)
22 They go around climbing (7)
23 She gives one cat a couple of points (6)
26 One might be given it in an observation (4)

63

ACROSS

6 Inviting us to further capers, it might be said (2, 4, 3, 5)
9 Such as may be suited for personal input (6)
10 They observe events from the west arch (8)
11 Clever enough to get on beside the sea (8)
13 External placing in production (6)
15 Lost like a good chap before seeing the light (6)
17 A spot of disgrace (6)
19 It just shows what's on offer (6)
20 Revealing a narrative talent? (4-4)
22 Getting rid of management? (8)
24 In time it will indicate the half-hour (6)
26 Time to take what's coming to you (11, 3)

DOWN

1 Not a periodical devoted to cosmetics (6, 8)
2 Clumsy fellow in a mopping-up operation (4)
3 Enrol for service at a trying time (6)
4 Better pair of spectacles broken in the salad (8)
5 In which it all comes out (4)
7 Pulling in the direction of a side (6)
8 Means of all-round communication (8, 6)
12 Dress for a rising personality? (3-2)
14 Not exactly generous in one's cups? (5)
16 A form of narrative that shows lack of appreciation (8)
18 She finds a hero in South Africa (6)
21 By itself making gradual progress (6)
23 You have to go when you get it (4)
25 One-horse race in the country (4)

64

ACROSS

1 Beastly account of the old showman? (7, 4)
9 Close of play (7)
10 Hair-cut on the roof? (7)
11 Not much affection at the end of the affaire! (3)
12 Happening to find that the record is poetry (7)
13 Treated warmly so trade can be arranged (7)
14 Face of a fool? (3)
15 Brown looks priggish in the water (5)
17 One doesn't feel at home in it (5)
18 Underworld character in outer space (5)
20 Valued Edward as an artist (5)
22 A lot of talk about fuel (3)
24 Country hotel so disorganised! (7)
25 Starting price on a racehorse to perform brilliantly (7)
26 Crazy fellow possibly getting tight (3)
27 Nothing to fasten one on in view (7)
28 He makes a cross decision (7)
29 Vital encounter in a knitting tournament? (6, 5)

DOWN

1 Problem raised in the fuel debate? (7, 8)
2 Signal the wrong son to produce the bottles (7)
3 One goes in to make the princess a showgirl (5)
4 Noticing the former pupil needs an attendant (9)
5 Follow one road to the gallery (7)
6 Quick drawing of a stormy scene? (9, 6)
7 Funny way to get the best! (6)
8 Interfere with what sounds like an award (6)
16 People in the army (9)
18 Trundle up after the old man presents a sickly
   appearance (6)
19 Sketch of the escape route? (7)
21 It's the talk of the region! (7)
23 Drink given to a cobbler (6)
25 Pre-departure get-up (5)

65

ACROSS

1 He doesn't read everything, being top man (7)
5 Buttonhole Bill Price (6)
9 Afraid of getting the shakes? (7)
10 Talking a lot about action? (7)
11 Get involved in forming a link (3)
12 Nicer secret revealed in town (11)
13 Being as you are (5)
14 Are they taken to discover the depths of noise? (9)
16 Fellow worker having an association with an officer (9)
17 Number having a row (5)
19 They show ability to win university grants (11)
22 How Rosa might deceive another girl (3)
23 Evil Sue can be difficult to catch (7)
24 Part of a group that includes FBI operators (7)
26 He takes great interest in one's difficulties (6)
27 Dog of a Siberian! (7)

DOWN

1 Cause devilish discomfort? (7)
2 When one hasn't much time before dawn? (2, 3, 5, 5)
3 Mean not to try to be a friend (3)
4 Early warning of a school of acting on the river (5)
5 Exciting time with a publicity attempt (9)
6 It takes one round the bend! (5)
7 Where you'd expect to see some killing pictures? (8, 7)
8 They give us regular beatings (6)
12 No ace can be shuffled in water (5)
14 These rigs baffle the viewer (9)
15 Straighten the line of a garment (5)
16 Able to find the bar after taking quite a lot (6)
18 Handled one man at a different rate (7)
20 Pipe plant (5)
21 Nothing a relative can provide in place of refreshment (5)
25 They swear by it in the north! (3)

66

ACROSS

1 Plate showing cricket bat maker's design? (6, 7)
8 Circumstantial accompaniment (4)
9 Back me and put money in to obtain growth (3)
10 She finds Hamlet quite diverting (6)
11 River Elbe's diverted so that it can flow back? (10)
13 In a national song contest too! (4)
14 Pet drinker? (6)
16 Not known to have been christened? (8)
19 Rate poet poorly for having written this (8)
22 One's sorry to do so (6)
25 Hardy heroine (4)
26 Tied up for a time in fascination? (10)
27 Supporter providing a tablet for the artist's comeback (6)
28 Not much of a society started by a fool (3)
29 Work on quarters anyone can enter (4)
30 It hides the killer's identity (6, 7)

DOWN

1 Sergeant-major taking over a more complicated rocket range (7)
2 Get the message in an unsound way (3-4)
3 Too much vision could be a mistake! (9)
4 She has a plan to put up (3)
5 Let it be used as identification (5)
6 Vision of a sound cockney drink (7)
7 Fate points to trouble I am in (7)
12 It's bound to give cover (7)
15 In the sky it's unrealised hope (3)
17 Makes right and wrong judgments (9)
18 Something woolly out of the west (3)
20 More than you bargained for, perhaps (7)
21 Not quite a silent thief (7)
23 Demonstrate inner approval just to annoy (7)
24 Sister has her place here (7)
26 It's fun to look round Park Royal (5)
28 Miss Farrow put up to be objective (3)

67

ACROSS

1 High official who appoints the officers? (12)
8 Singular pace of a dance (3-4)
9 Dog giving directions (7)
11 Moon starer he could well be (10)
12 Source of revolutionary music? (4)
14 Made progress as an itinerant player? (8)
16 False point amid the lunar wreckage (6)
17 One sees it in a rage (3)
19 Alkali deposit on a vessel (6)
21 Sensible ground for identifying a simpleton (8)
24 Eyes heavenly bodies (4)
25 Stirring up dirt on cads doesn't create harmony (10)
27 Sounding off by way of a reprimand (7)
28 Rain too can be found here (7)
29 Understood to be included (12)

DOWN

1 Shout about a street in the city (7)
2 Still advising us not to gesticulate too much (10)
3 A mischief-maker and a wanderer but he'll get better (8)
4 One way to be superior after tea (6)
5 All-round row in Valhalla (4)
6 Went around in the east to get weaving (7)
7 What is expected from a high-minded henchman? (5, 7)
10 It comes to mind about passing the plate (12)
13 Poorly valued when lowly assessed? (10)
15 Overnight deposit (3)
18 Show how to take a break from the Cod Isles (8)
20 Smoke plant (7)
22 Given support at a sitting? (7)
23 One who isn't returning? (6)
26 Drag along with no hard feeling (4)

68

ACROSS

6 Is he employed to find out where the criminal lives? (5, 9)
9 Island of various haunts (6)
10 Each different nuisance claims minimum cost (8)
11 No use going without footwear (8)
13 Just the thing to get you in! (6)
15 Agree to perform about a hundred on record (6)
17 Chemical making some of the chalk a little soft (6)
19 Swindler's tool? (6)
20 Hard to deviate from the Bute road (8)
22 Penned and sent with a letter (8)
24 Having grown to show mother the true difference (6)
26 Fuddy-duddy hidden by a paper (6, 3, 5)

DOWN

1 Only spirit making success at all possible? (5, 2, 1, 6)
2 Dawn goddess dropping gold in the air (4)
3 Creature with a hang-over? (6)
4 Lead pets around the base (8)
5 Don't go on holding up vessels (4)
7 One tax to cut (6)
8 Personal stake in the underwear industry? (6, 8)
12 Fastens on a change of course? (5)
14 A job to support the professor? (5)
16 Friend having different ideas for defence (8)
18 A question of method had to be raised over the elephant (6)
21 Man turning up in brief do-it-yourself material (6)
23 Retreat from Baudelaire's romanticism (4)
25 I'm to be thanked for becoming domesticated (4)

69

ACROSS

1 Bar supporter on a sporting occasion (8)
5 Old chap at the end of a line (6)
9 Go up and down in getting along (8)
10 Shows a vessel around the harbour (6)
12 Surprise at the lack of air? (4)
13 Such a question you need not answer (10)
15 Soldiers fought to get them on the flag (6, 7)
19 It shows what a carry-on there can be (9, 4)
23 Covering a leap as a slight aid to timekeeping (10)
25 Animals coming back a pace (4)
28 Share it with Nora somehow (6)
29 Step down if bad at ice mixing (8)
30 He'll find a home after finishing dinner (6)
31 A lass one takes round for part of the year (8)

DOWN

1 Injured party might bear it (6)
2 High points of a clandestine meeting (5)
3 Not intending to be mother, one takes it (4)
4 Case of the bookie's cash (7)
6 A meal doesn't get started in this class (5)
7 Where service is available for the low in spirit (9)
8 Always moving to get the others a reduction (8)
11 Urge to come up to scratch? (4)
14 Cause commotion in prison (4)
15 The show jumping game? (9)
16 Other instances could be given in a wretched recital (3)
17 Want of a proverbial friend (4)
18 Is it ridden by one of those fabulous marines? (3-5)
20 Grumble about an informer (4)
21 Give title to superiority (7)
22 Attraction of another hearing (6)
24 It's sometimes a job to fill them (5)
26 Man standing up before getting in a conveyance (5)
27 Partial lack of balance (4)

70

ACROSS

1 It offers a chance to get in the swim (7, 4)
9 Struggle to be earthy about sex appeal (7)
10 Susceptible to a touch of diplomacy? (7)
11 Time to grow old? (3)
12 Turns to stare improperly (7)
13 Mass turn-out to see the girl — she's so good-looking! (7)
14 Point back where there's something to eat (3)
15 Gun to bring a flier crashing (5)
17 Sound medical man with singular following (5)
18 Pull up when there's some difficulty (5)
20 Goes right on the wrong side (5)
22 Move up and down to dock (3)
24 No charge for such a small amount of matter (7)
25 The food is in keeping here (7)
26 Well contrasted (3)
27 Trying to get an interview with royalty (7)
28 Satisfy with a very quiet facility (7)
29 Go ahead and steal from a roof, it might appear (4, 3, 4)

DOWN

1 Means of inflicting pointless injury? (5, 10)
2 Disloyal fomenter of art riot (7)
3 Turn aside for inspiration (5)
4 Openings at the top in the north (9)
5 Fruity alternative offered in Somerset (7)
6 Painter given the bird in town (8, 7)
7 Gem of an insect (6)
8 Distinctive part of a revolution (6)
16 Bed and breakfast at the castle? It seems like weeks! (9)
18 Reliable quarters in the army (6)
19 The girl's straw identified by the poet (7)
21 Point of piety (7)
23 Exchange with an American saloon keeper endlessly (6)
25 An old one used to display some warmth (5)

71

ACROSS

1 He provides a contemporary account first after the attack is thrown back (7)
5 A noise to frighten people? (6)
9 Peculiar rag sent out (7)
10 Something to read before the features (7)
11 Give vent to some music (3)
12 Fighting cover (11)
13 You've an even chance of getting the number repeated (5)
14 Clean corridor of power? (9)
16 Attacking with a tendency to fashionable oaths? (9)
17 Trade union party right in the royal house (5)
19 Nothing at all wrong with her behaviour! (7, 4)
22 She occupies part of the bridal suite (3)
23 It's smart to have a try in the Middle West (7)
24 Trousers on the stove in Surrey? (7)
26 Public service conductor (6)
27 Showed the question to have been put before? (7)

DOWN

1 Ladies this side, please (7)
2 Basis for flying away from the land (8, 7)
3 It accommodates members of the bar, naturally (3)
4 River engineers taking round explosive (5)
5 Pure evil's unattractive form (9)
6 Put your foot on the tyre? (5)
7 Simple diet for the multitude (6, 3, 6)
8 Explosive creature in a pop song? (6)
12 Noble Russian lad with rising artist (5)
14 There's a body underneath (9)
15 Way to get in after a city business victory (5)
16 One member has a performance that can be a hit (6)
18 Responded with another performance (7)
20 Don't meet a girl starting to make demands (5)
21 Ability to lose a thousand dollars as you go along (5)
25 French town that lacks something? (3)

72

ACROSS

1 Angry determination to be king? (6, 7)
8 Explosive haircut (4)
9 Front or rear vehicle (3)
10 Complain about the game? (6)
11 Source of the spirit (10)
13 Thought I would start eating (4)
14 Brides unsettled by the ruins (6)
16 Claim a Yorkshire town lacks aspiration (8)
19 Suggestion in favour of distributing opals (8)
22 Allows people on the move to dispense with the motorway (6)
25 Sketch showing where the aircraft lost direction (4)
26 Passing caress by a swimmer? (4-6)
27 Guess he must be a minister (6)
28 Point of a dancer (3)
29 A cracked nut in the family (4)
30 Dirty old sailors giving faint stimulus? (8-5)

DOWN

1 Cash in on your understanding? (7)
2 The girl's form after dieting? (7)
3 No doubt they have new tales to tell (9)
4 Make a point of providing some beer (3)
5 So like a horse to be wet! (5)
6 Pressing on beyond a wash (7)
7 Way the rise is coming into being (7)
12 Allowed when a girl was wounded (7)
15 Expression of disapproval to Ted when kicked (3)
17 Enters as a guest (9)
18 Did she cause a German writer to lose his head? (3)
20 The right friends for gatherings (7)
21 Thoughtful writers I've become attached to (7)
23 Sky writing? (3, 4)
24 Receipts for which you can thank royalties (7)
26 Ammunition to protect some nut? (5)
28 Can this be money? (3)

73

ACROSS

1 Phantom of the theatre (7, 5)
8 Cutting down growth on the personal front (7)
9 Dance of singular brevity (7)
11 Speak of putting in joints? (10)
12 Prize for achievement, one takes it (4)
14 The house is home to him (8)
16 Stick where we are now (6)
17 Note to perform with aspiration (3)
19 Beginning of an unfashionable group? (6)
21 It's seen at the end of the tunnel (8)
24 Pig it in a bar (4)
25 He hopes to be a winner (10)
27 Got a tub round to pull others (3-4)
28 Otherwise one has no business in the river (7)
29 Behind the curtain he's in charge (5-7)

DOWN

1 Capable of being moulded finally into a small representation (7)
2 Rules for curling the lip when royal people are around (10)
3 Flung about in the rising river and swallowed up (8)
4 The're not worn for long surely? (6)
5 Pay attention when he gets to be top man on paper (4)
6 Day one had a meal to provide more than enough (7)
7 It's his business to make a getaway (12)
10 Making an introduction is a gift (12)
13 Losing one's grip on things (10)
15 Punishing piece of production (3)
18 What a difference when there's an instrument in the hedge! (8)
20 Just an idea albeit giving Tom a start (7)
22 For Olga rum may have some attraction (7)
23 You can only go up from here (6)
26 This way it's no good offering entertainment (4)

74

ACROSS

6 In the unlikely event of an opportunity to get away? (2, 3, 3-6)
9 It's not alone on the beach (6)
10 Getting along like a two-year-old (8)
11 Living like a god (8)
13 In this home a great amount is insufficient (6)
15 More demanding character in a musical (6)
17 Write a letter at a stroke (6)
19 Bad luck if it's hard! (6)
20 Time to find a way over including an award (8)
22 Great performer in the water? (8)
24 Bill takes him to be absolutely right (6)
26 Let the chap get wind of a powerful sea-shanty? (4, 3, 3, 4)

DOWN

1 Married life could start here temporarily (9, 5)
2 Tear off and leave it (4)
3 He is in superlative command (6)
4 Purely formal in the Burlington House manner? (8)
5 The way everything can be built up (4)
7 Fine state to be in! (6)
8 Source of inner warmth (7, 7)
12 Give a view of work in the Orient (5)
14 It might arouse a fearful state (5)
16 Seeing a number about to agree (8)
18 Song of national standing (6)
21 Empty container inside another (6)
23 Conducts a quarrel along certain lines (4)
25 Cheat a bird (4)

75

ACROSS

1 Body of a flier (3-5)
5 He had stable employment at the inn (6)
9 Boring quality that makes little Maureen refuse a man (8)
10 Just a little bit of egotism or selfishness (6)
12 Returning in an emotional state to accept one's fate (4)
13 Making the diver sit up by causing trouble (10)
15 Infinitely extended at the end of the yard? (6, 7)
19 There's no work for her to do (4, 2, 7)
23 Thinking of those wheels going round? (10)
25 Keep on and on at the instrument? (4)
28 Vulgar business of twisting ears (6)
29 Reduce it in the motorway opening (8)
30 It's smarter to ride it around (6)
31 Supporter of one who is lying (8)

DOWN

1 A drama involving the fleet (6)
2 Music for a man to perform (5)
3 Sounds the proper thing to do (4)
4 House where a chap is turned on (7)
6 Pick up something exclusive (5)
7 Weakness of being a girl? (9)
8 Anxiety ended by the new sentry (8)
11 It takes some beating! (4)
14 He's beginning in pretty rough conditions (4)
15 Doesn't he protect his master's head? (9)
16 Expected at some suitable time (3)
17 Lily displays a certain spirit (4)
18 It's lucky you can't see it in the dark (5, 3)
20 Determined at last to make an instrument (4)
21 Worship a new development of the oil side (7)
22 Feast of butter? (6)
24 Try to take in a little (5)
26 Knowing a struggle has some point (5)
27 In what one writes one doesn't make a hit (4)

76

ACROSS

1 Striking encounter between kings? (6, 5)
9 Bob around in a circle taking money (7)
10 Burden the little Father with a number (7)
11 Behave like a lost sheep (3)
12 Has a swell time speaking (7)
13 He wants to know where the money went (7)
14 Time to give direction to an artist (3)
15 Charming in a small way (5)
17 Expired right inside for lack of water (5)
18 Does it enable one to grasp what the waves are saying? (5)
20 Lines of peaks and points (5)
22 Missing place in France (3)
24 Something left when one's gone (7)
25 Scolds for putting an animal among insects (7)
26 Put to work in an upper-class household (3)
27 The girl with rare distinction who can take away the wool (7)
28 The part that gets cut? (7)
29 Monarchy established in the next world (7-4)

DOWN

1 Blow-out with a sound fry-up (6-3-6)
2 The list symbolically altered in Scotland (7)
3 Boxes in a dramatic situation (5)
4 Didn't try to reform a rare fiend (9)
5 Gave a profit on surrender? (7)
6 Quick industrial action in a stormy situation? (9, 6)
7 Game a girl hasn't quite finished (6)
8 Strode around in confinement until needed (6)
16 Given a break (9)
18 Hearty nonsense about transport (6)
19 Go too far in a successful attack? (7)
21 Wind, my dear fellow, takes the company up and down! (7)
23 Putting the question of a model's activity? (6)
25 Twigs the woman is a slattern? (5)

77

ACROSS

1 Took it easy when the question was put again (7)
5 What you get for what you do (6)
9 Girl to turn to later (7)
10 This one is happening now (7)
11 In favour of being paid! (3)
12 Aged sucker needing no instruction (11)
13 Remove all traces of the times on the way (5)
14 Where an association can get across in Surrey (9)
16 Transmission by actors with heavy dialect? (9)
17 Put under cover for most of the season (5)
19 On which overheads may become a burden? (7-4)
22 Good for the curate in part (3)
23 To save coming back I have become inclined to dodge (7)
24 Space to deploy some oar in the water (3-4)
26 Where ghosts can usually be seen? (6)
27 Nash is about to refuse French water in Ireland (7)

DOWN

1 Go wrong again and get worse (7)
2 The unacceptable face of diplomacy (7, 3, 5)
3 Ready for collection? (3)
4 Mad RA collapse sensation! (5)
5 Turn and move aimlessly in the spray (9)
6 To catch a girl give her a ring (5)
7 Have great aspirations as an astronaut? (5, 3, 3, 4)
8 The way a communist looked (6)
12 Want of a note on the woodwind (5)
14 Nothing said before tucking in — how inelegant! (9)
15 Many find skating a refreshment (5)
16 Be effective up to a degree in dancing (6)
18 Government course of treatment? (7)
20 Some deception when starting to name a foreigner (5)
21 What idiots girls are when they lose their heads! (5)
25 You may have read about him in a magazine (3)

78

ACROSS

1 Girl giving a talk might add piquancy to a meal (5, 8)
8 Get into shape to support a sitting (4)
9 A fool from his appearance (3)
10 Having been given striking evidence of superiority (6)
11 Make-up as an old soldier might confront the enemy (4-6)
13 One front is Russian (4)
14 Pay to do it up in Yorkshire (6)
16 Beat seen not to be here (8)
19 He gives the land a professional look (8)
22 She finds a chap a bit daft (6)
25 Mark the way to a vehicle (4)
26 Strange about the royal groom being so clever! (10)
27 Outcome of an Ulster upheaval (6)
28 Some sort of jacket in green? (3)
29 Pride of the team (4)
30 Leftist guidance when Britain gets going? (4, 2, 3, 4)

DOWN

1 Keeping wise about height (7)
2 Licking little animal? (7)
3 Coy diver's strange find (9)
4 Epitaph for a young tearaway (3)
5 By no means extravagant change of robes (5)
6 A foreigner shows it to two men (7)
7 Handy missile (7)
12 Not very bright about an Indian city plan (7)
15 Pitch of the road (3)
17 Domestic flight (9)
18 Negative rise in weight (3)
20 Thick soup? It isn't quite apparent (7)
21 Having the effect of goodness? (7)
23 A girl taking ten in Italy (7)
24 Deceived by a common peer in action (7)
26 The proportion that's changed to air (5)
28 Drug some tea? (3)

79

ACROSS

1 Scruple Lefty treated with proper consideration (12)
8 Many are found to follow Leviticus (7)
9 Basis for choosing one's colours (7)
11 He'll make the final arrangements (10)
12 Note an inscription that will hold attention (4)
14 Ammunition in the news (8)
16 He drops a line in the hope of some response (6)
17 Creature made a meal of the clergyman (3)
19 Just the place for the undercover shopper (6)
21 Marge allowed to return to convey a message (8)
24 Study with an egghead a possible storm signal (4)
25 Argument about what's inside? (10)
27 One sail reset by a nautical celebrity? (3-4)
28 Eric's confused in some degree in Italy (7)
29 Striking means of improving on the usual covering? (6-6)

DOWN

1 Give new shape that might make me older (7)
2 Leads attack on points? (10)
3 Delighted to find part of the city still (8)
4 Point to an animal showing some fur (6)
5 Does such a customer make trouble for the beauty parlour? (4)
6 Subsequently finding a pound on the side (7)
7 Claims and dependants make progress difficult (12)
10 Trying to see if a one-time fairy is unbalanced (12)
13 The confining of people within some abbey ruins (10)
15 Fastener for the head? (3)
18 For a tenant with a real bent for conversion (8)
20 Unable to give a word of thanks for the composition (7)
22 Vehicle proceeding on certain lines (4-3)
23 Not her turn to buzz around! (6)
26 Have trouble moving when lacking rigidity (4)

80

ACROSS

6 He feels at home in the house (3, 2, 3, 6)
9 No end of a position (6)
10 Brings hands together approvingly (8)
11 Went up as the century finished (8)
13 Persuade to bring on (6)
15 The fellow from France? (6)
17 Mark Joe coming back on the street with a parent (6)
19 Depression after an attack, perhaps (6)
20 Think how one might have got at ice (8)
22 He has some hopes (8)
24 Somehow my rise doesn't bring happiness (6)
26 A drink from it might promote better feeling (8, 6)

DOWN

1 By Friday, he got the help he needed (8, 6)
2 The man in front is in it (4)
3 Cause annoyance by going into a dive? (6)
4 Reproduction isn't on letterpress (8)
5 She turns me up by becoming a mother (4)
7 Doesn't throw away a broken ash rod (6)
8 She had a novel lover (4, 10)
12 Don't start to be sorry for a bird (5)
14 Finger some advice about the garden (5)
16 Stirring raid leading to a movement in the sea (8)
18 With a little science they can be made to mow (6)
21 Sounds a chancy way to frolic (6)
23 One small relative is a goddess! (4)
25 Place to take it easy on the way (4)

81

ACROSS

1 What a disaster for Jane in the West! (8)
5 Got along in the morning to be given the leech treatment (6)
9 The sort of love one may hunger for? (8)
10 Investigates an expert who isn't quite the best (6)
12 Light joinery? (4)
13 Chap in rugs going around accumulating stock (10)
15 Guess there's going to be a fight? (5, 8)
19 It may get off the ground in a small way (5, 8)
23 Children at last get applause for smartening up (10)
25 Put Barry's head in the drink if you can! (4)
28 Such a song might be a lullaby (6)
29 Work on the river place across the way (8)
30 Catch the girl in a lower position (6)
31 Associate briefly with FBI operatives inside for a bit (8)

DOWN

1 Laugh like a goose (6)
2 Flower raised inside but nothing up outside (5)
3 Sullen form of verb? (4)
4 Finished doing something penetrating? (7)
6 Black girl by whom one might be quite carried away? (5)
7 It might reduce friction during the revolution (9)
8 He has an idea of how things ought to look (8)
11 Apostolic legislation? (4)
14 Most of the ship is in port (4)
15 Turned and found to be superfluous (9)
16 It's thickened by a blow (3)
17 Confession of cowardice in the Middle East (4)
18 A nice arm twisting display by a foreigner (8)
20 Spot ten at rising (4)
21 Hack means of transport? (7)
22 Building material brings me in little money (6)
24 It's what one hopes to get for money (5)
26 She'd get well in prison (5)
27 Wish to be extended (4)

82

ACROSS

1 They should have an electrifying effect on the enemy (5-6)
9 Moral doubt carrying little weight? (7)
10 Ian's turn to give his ancestry new colour (7)
11 Animal in a vessel (3)
12 The sort of squad that always gets it wrong (7)
13 Have trouble getting the speech started (7)
14 A long time to change one (3)
15 Like a judge without drink? (5)
17 Don't start a meal near the centre (5)
18 Foundation for bachelor girl (5)
20 Try leaving the trade for the river (5)
22 Covering membership of the team (3)
24 Body under a balloon (7)
25 One doesn't get it from a yes-man (7)
26 Nothing in a short weekend to cause unhappiness (3)
27 Mean for time about a girl (7)
28 Distorting what's true after reaching a point of agony (7)
29 It doesn't make much difference if you've only little money (5, 6)

DOWN

1 Triumph of the non-worker? (8, 7)
2 No sharp adjustment for the motherless (7)
3 Work to make some dough (5)
4 Confirmed as certain to be in colour (9)
5 Part of the oil outfit a French friend shows to be folding (7)
6 An alternative to a bathing-dress? (8, 7)
7 Grounds for thinking one's landed (6)
8 He may have security in hand (6)
16 Prison that kept the wife healthy? (9)
18 Don't allow any change in the tree (6)
19 Fruit of a Middle East marriage? (7)
21 Colour for fans to change (7)
23 Everyone in a bad temper on a bed (6)
25 Try to throw up in secret chagrin (5)

83

ACROSS

1 Results obtained by blowing? (7)
5 Not much of a spread in this predicament (6)
9 Occasion for pushing the boat out (7)
10 One may be lucky to get a dip in here (4-3)
11 Punishing touch of the sun? (3)
12 Rules covering routine slag removal (11)
13 In line with part of the Russian enterprise (5)
14 They're put on to exert influence (9)
16 Fixed idea of attack from outside (9)
17 Put away under cover (5)
19 Giving birth to fiction in a sneaky way? (4-7)
22 Not even a fellow in society (3)
23 It used to be enough to be followed (7)
24 It enables one to carry on (7)
26 Offer not to be rough (6)
27 Not far into drink on this occasion (7)

DOWN

1 Rate bit out for clerical cover (7)
2 Call to start something dramatic (9, 6)
3 Everything one might bid for (3)
4 Talk in the other fellow's language (5)
5 Tale Burns adapted for an officer (9)
6 Heat as in decay (5)
7 Decline of the spirit limiting one's movements (6, 9)
8 Insults in the language Jack employs (6)
12 Victoria's state briefly set up in ceremonies (5)
14 Ship a soldier with the Queen (9)
15 Pendulum music? (5)
16 Opportunity to make a getaway (6)
18 So happy to be providing warmth all round? (7)
20 Creature given double support (5)
21 Among the group providing a small picture (5)
25 You can tell if she puts on weight (3)

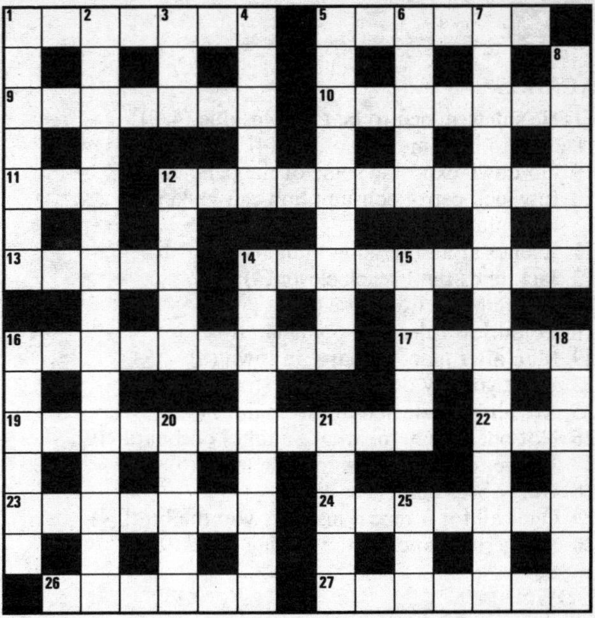
1
2
3
4
5
6
7
8
9
10
11
12
13
14
15
16
17
18
19
20
21
22
23
24
25
26
27

84

ACROSS

1 He's determined to be given his due (4, 9)
8 Said to be some sort of test (4)
9 Go down exposing some of the pebbles (3)
10 In which petrol consumption can be kept to a minimum (6)
11 It's not at all the same thing! (10)
13 Jack finds the French clever (4)
14 Where Mary was Rose (6)
16 Colourless rules of a politician (8)
19 Man after man, perhaps, in town (8)
22 What you lay on may cause strain (6)
25 Are all wars started in this region? (4)
26 Not one to pay for what he takes on board (10)
27 Where to find the fashionable team (6)
28 Hurry back for the cask (3)
29 One call for a repeat just gets you the bird! (4)
30 Staggering dance of the rowing men? (9, 4)

DOWN

1 More like crossroads work? (7)
2 Like a bundle of malice? (7)
3 Depressed at getting no applause? (9)
4 High ball with which one might get by in the hall (3)
5 Flying standard? (5)
6 Domestic line-up (7)
7 A big cigar and other royal privileges (7)
12 Out of the running at this time and place (7)
15 Come up for it out of a dive (3)
17 Noel's nice, maybe, but may display rudeness (9)
18 Take shelter from the German battle fleet (3)
20 Set an artist up on the mountains (7)
21 What you'd expect when a point is put into a limb! (7)
23 Understand how to turn assets into cash (7)
24 Slap ice in an odd way (7)
26 Wood taken from port in ships (5)
28 Favouring demonstration without trial (3)

85

ACROSS

1 Mark, for instance, a former top policeman (12)
8 More can be made of this story (7)
9 Sign of private advancement (7)
11 To the French a share shows forbearance (10)
12 Impact of the wind (4)
14 Living in a ship, navigators use them (8)
16 General return of pictures shortly before ten (6)
17 It's said to be quite agreeable (3)
19 To some degree Mac may bring you luck (6)
21 He has a job to keep afloat (8)
24 Dora's about to find the way (4)
25 Relative security? (10)
27 She's got it coming to her! (7)
28 Ivan too comes round to show appreciation (7)
29 Variously located at the points indicated (4, 3, 5)

DOWN

1 Involved business with a politician over Roman law (7)
2 Not one of the big guns of the church, one hears (5, 5)
3 It's a matter of who you are (8)
4 Dry on the hill in one area (6)
5 Start work giving directions (4)
6 Does it give a warm reception to what one hears? (3-4)
7 Steps taken to demonstrate dissent (7, 5)
10 Discovery in Canada by travellers fresh from Britain? (12)
13 Cut ace, a ten to emphasize there's been a shuffle! (10)
15 Put the needle in at several points (3)
18 Workers here have the makings of craft movement (4-4)
20 Naval team's holiday location? (7)
22 Chance of raiment for a girl (7)
23 Singularly choice personality (6)
26 Historian lying on one point (4)

86

ACROSS

6 Sticky manifestation of one quarter of the class difference (9, 5)
9 Allow what may be held after starting tea (6)
10 The writing on the building (8)
11 French poetry in a genuine turnaround (8)
13 Obtain what's essential to provide spirits (6)
15 Raise a hand to one's superior (6)
17 Leader of a flock (6)
19 It may hold up progress on the railway (6)
20 Flexible arrangement for providing liquid (8)
22 Impact he made in strong terms (8)
24 Beginning with an unfashionable group (6)
26 Difficulty ahead for a major retailer? (7, 2, 5)

DOWN

1 His is a hard way to avoid ferry charges (7, 7)
2 Gathering to make an impact (4)
3 One may be at one's lowest, though, when on them (6)
4 End lyric badly in the tube (8)
5 Give top performance in a custard-pie comedy (4)
7 It might be dopey to put it in (6)
8 An evil one might give them his people's trouble (14)
12 The Spanish chap shortly becoming a girl (5)
14 Very much inclined to be pricey (5)
16 Revealing a narrative ability? (4-4)
18 Affected to be smart (6)
21 Works up to employ a partner (6)
23 Time I left that alluring woman! (4)
25 East end fellow in the city (4)

87

ACROSS

1 It may show how low the level has fallen (8)
5 You can count on it to assist calculation (6)
9 Alter inn so that it's not the same inside (8)
10 Crazy Margaret provides a certain flavour (6)
12 Just like him to be before his time! (4)
13 Engine dirt might be part of the mixture (10)
15 Run a bit for an extra large helping (6, 7)
19 Can't be made to look old-hat? (13)
23 Put back the curb, it's said (10)
25 Incautious start for a top person (4)
28 They're all on the same level (6)
29 Palace depicted by bad Balham artist (8)
30 Arrange a golf device to take one's weight (6)
31 It was instrumental in combining rest and play (8)

DOWN

1 Club the man behind the wheel (6)
2 He gets out to fade away (5)
3 Time for a word (4)
4 One of the usual means of communication (7)
6 Certain to be tied up (5)
7 MBE nicely presented to the old king (9)
8 Seeing something to heave with a metallic note (8)
11 Fall for an excursion? (4)
14 He may be booted on the stage (4)
15 It's hard to be unco-operative (9)
16 I myself must find a way to move (3)
17 Girl in red (4)
18 Cuts up about accommodation? (8)
20 Land terrorists at the Pole (4)
21 Tries to get a reaction in the Isle of Wight? (7)
22 Any car brought round for a singer? (6)
24 Sort out some tangled loves (5)
26 Change for one pound if you're good (5)
27 Great Chinese build-up (4)

88

ACROSS

1 Relatively unattractive figures of traditional entertainment (4, 7)
9 Car dial registering very substantial change (7)
10 Beaming all round with happiness (7)
11 By way of a partial deviation (3)
12 Mother having a queer turn in the tent (7)
13 She finds her man when there's a horse around (7)
14 Fodder returned to express defiance (3)
15 Hold-up in the studio (5)
17 Order wrongly cited (5)
18 Pull two ways in urban settings (5)
20 Border on the limit (5)
22 It produces its producer (3)
24 He smoothes the way for the traveller (7)
25 Many take to a girl in the city (7)
26 As well as amounting to nothing (3)
27 Make mad attempt to prevent the door opening? (7)
28 Gestures indicating Tom is on the wrong tack (7)
29 Those exercising pupil power? (6, 5)

DOWN

1 None too healthy with wind and rain overhead? (5, 3, 7)
2 Cut reel to make provision for talk (7)
3 Recover five in a business offer (5)
4 It makes talk incomprehensible to others (9)
5 Sign as giving approval (7)
6 They tell the actors where to go (5, 10)
7 Not at all pleased to have some steak inside (6)
8 The way to baffle the setter (6)
16 A number observed around the sports item (9)
18 Twist of the necklace (6)
19 Likely to start something (7)
21 Choose a new academician as a figure of tragedy (7)
23 His rag turns out to be rather showy (6)
25 Amusing award given to one in the County Council (5)

89

ACROSS

1 There's big trouble when it goes up! (7)
5 It may be said to create an opening (6)
9 Gifts of parable (7)
10 Assumed to have got the idea (7)
11 Such timing is deceptive (3)
12 Madness as an entertainment (11)
13 Go on playing cricket for the staff (5)
14 Rose gets involved with Teddy and is ruined (9)
16 Exaggerates ability to pay taxes? (9)
17 Punished for getting the dance wrong (5)
19 Not all there — only in bits (11)
22 Frenchman losing weight — it's all talk! (3)
23 Prison exponent of the big fiddle? (7)
24 Prisoner in a hat showing cultivation (7)
26 Pearl's protector (6)
27 Given a line as in a statement of beliefs (7)

DOWN

1 It enables one to get immersed in domestic life (7)
2 Flower girl in some depression (4, 2, 3, 6)
3 You'll have to cheese off Brownie! (3)
4 They have an inquisitive following (5)
5 The day a girl stands a good man up they take off! (9)
6 Not the excitable type (5)
7 It enables one to take the larger view (10, 5)
8 Attacked for having taken too much? (6)
12 He gives a man an alternative (5)
14 Too ardent revolutionary means to start an explosion (9)
15 Hard to describe some mountains (5)
16 Where one works when not skating (6)
18 Swell thing to do! (7)
20 Little Maureen at first seems a bit wet (5)
21 Room for some salty wit? (5)
25 Laurie may be slumbering with a snake around him (3)

90

ACROSS

1 Where one might get taken by a violent train of events (6-7)
8 A hit with a hair-style? (4)
9 Put away in a leather bag (3)
10 Feature of the country where life is said to have pace? (6)
11 Payment for adapting screen poem (10)
13 Lily wants some sport in the morning (4)
14 Stuck in the mud or settled deep in the West Country (6)
16 Superior people who have greatness thrust upon them? (8)
19 It's a way back, chum — that's my guess! (8)
22 Collector's item (6)
25 Story of the lost city of wisdom (4)
26 Obstinate Edward returning dressed in fur (10)
27 This Scotsman knows it's cheaper by rail! (6)
28 Resort in a foreign country (3)
29 Lisp a salutation to friends (4)
30 He gives one a clearer outlook (6-7)

DOWN

1 Prescription for patient satisfaction (7)
2 Old soldiers in large numbers (7)
3 Was London needled by her? (9)
4 Ready for some shooting? (3)
5 The wedding's up this way (5)
6 Nice lad in a cold climate (7)
7 Body of water? (7)
12 Nothing need be done to show it (7)
15 Depression on land in old shire (3)
17 Change a ten by turns (9)
18 Likely to go round without one animal (3)
20 A bird you can take in? (7)
21 Boy following it perhaps in a foreign language (7)
23 Afraid to use smart knowledge (7)
24 Man to make one cross (7)
26 Hidden animal on the move (5)
28 Dry when one's drinking (3)

91

ACROSS

1 You can't be sure he's safe (8, 4)
8 Went round with a buzz (7)
9 Feature of an animal in the meadow (7)
11 Reduced from a due extent, perhaps (10)
12 Supporter's joint (4)
14 Southern resort value in Gateshead (8)
16 Protects or threatens with a gun (6)
17 He's well known to have been refused (3)
19 He gets around outside the office (3-3)
21 Directly describing the end of civilisation or the Navy (8)
24 Island in an area of exceptional beauty (4)
25 It's kind to a literary man to provide a machine (10)
27 Master of music (7)
28 Symbol of the Scots' prickly character? (7)
29 They're suited in two colours (7-5)

DOWN

1 Breeze for a drink (7)
2 Not in a rich mixture of style (10)
3 Coat put on the pillar-box (3, 5)
4 Changed course when it was fixed? (6)
5 Repeatedly puts one's oar in (4)
6 It never gets a hearing (7)
7 That nice boy in the garden (5-7)
10 Erin's a staple for jokes (12)
13 It should be able to unearth the quarry (3-7)
15 Information as to when a girl leaves the city (3)
18 Turn over disc to me at home (8)
20 Refined fellow with a fish (7)
22 Lands in Oriental countries (7)
23 Magnate having business on with half the City (6)
26 No flying visit (4)

92

ACROSS

6 President and patriarch in the city (7, 7)
9 By which expansion may be measured (6)
10 You'll find him quite enlightening (8)
11 Coy limbs disposed to mean something (8)
13 Make lace also for personal adornment (6)
15 Having attained a superior position (6)
17 Clever enough to get on in a resort (6)
19 Something must happen at this point (6)
20 I am getting stout as a business man (8)
22 Urge to vote a cad out of position (8)
24 In which one may finally get carried away (6)
26 Undesirable commercial practice of an Egyptian confidence trickster? (7, 7)

DOWN

1 There'll be a good morrow after this occasion (6, 8)
2 Supporter going over (4)
3 Cheat out of a tool? (6)
4 Girl up the wrong tree in some measure (8)
5 Picture of one swindle (4)
7 Many take a girl to be showing ill-will (6)
8 Ennobled jeweller brought to book? (4, 2, 3, 5)
12 Go up in a vehicle? Not really! (5)
14 Creature of a fearsome stripe (5)
16 Cite acts that have made us happy (8)
18 Various people who go below (6)
21 Preserve from a troublesome child (6)
23 Ring a fellow in the Middle East (4)
25 Not a serious journey (4)

93

ACROSS

1 Send secret communication that's easily sorted out (4, 4)
5 Hand-operated computer (6)
9 American Government get-together (8)
10 Have fun like a medical man in prison (6)
12 Way to a hide-out in the garden (4)
13 Male representative taking me in to the bosses (10)
15 His sophistication is global, it seems (3, 2, 3, 5)
19 Good advice from the sage (5, 2, 6)
23 Having points that might give a girl a turn (10)
25 Be against putting in an objection (4)
28 Greeted with a hard shower (6)
29 End of the line for a queen (8)
30 South of France study not anticipated (6)
31 Raise the number swallowed by a bird (8)

DOWN

1 Quite a lot to pay for cigarettes? (6)
2 Perception of wisdom? (5)
3 Old stuff from the farmer! (4)
4 This side for the ladies (7)
6 Put it on to cause a stoppage (5)
7 Bill turns up with a crooked gambler to give you the message (9)
8 You're on your own in this (8)
11 In which it all comes out (4)
14 The burden America bears (4)
15 Made to die with humiliation? (9)
16 Pull on pads in Cornwall (3)
17 Get along in town after Biggles (4)
18 Moves to turn darkness into light (8)
20 Just men in a novel (4)
21 Have something in mind (7)
22 Not easy ancestry to live with? (6)
24 She's relatively pleasant about the egghead (5)
26 Explode right in the bosom (5)
27 Beast among men (4)

94

ACROSS

1 Room girl in a domestic situation (7-4)
9 Consideration carrying little weight (7)
10 Get the height right in a carved figure (7)
11 Strike an understanding without drink (3)
12 The watchman's concern? (4-3)
13 Quarrelsome fellow making a fine Scots start (7)
14 Do it up after arguments (3)
15 Not one to turn his back when offered an affront (5)
17 Stop fighting and throw it in (5)
18 Cut up for a Christmas pie (5)
20 Some sort of cake for the egg producer (5)
22 Sing about it going down in the well (3)
24 A carless city has a job to spread out (7)
25 Holds quickly to some points (7)
26 Pass an officer shortly (3)
27 The Spanish agent has turned smart (7)
28 Shape what's intended (7)
29 No great expectation of dieting success? (7, 4)

DOWN

1 They're quite entertaining in a small way (10, 5)
2 Rebuke for an agent going over the top (7)
3 Not hidden above Ted's head (5)
4 Fruitful show of disapproval (9)
5 Girl meets chap, starts talking — but doesn't yield (7)
6 Repeated indication that a driver mustn't cross (6, 5, 4)
7 Additional message on charity in the Bible (6)
8 The reappearing spirit? (6)
16 Quite calm when they come for you? (9)
18 One of the crazier Reds (6)
19 You'd do better to see a bird after time (7)
21 Get up, my dear chap, and find a man to provide some food (7)
23 Made affectionate contact (6)
25 Knock down to the lowest level (5)

95

ACROSS

1 Slate the right animal (7)
5 Florence's family given less than the full dosage (6)
9 Levy not adapted for the new situation (7)
10 He must learn how to cope with a crash at Aintree (7)
11 It's just a little boring (3)
12 One doesn't expect to be seen in it (11)
13 He took a revolutionary line on the way (5)
14 Fresh accommodation for defenders in the North (9)
16 Brilliance on the screen at night? (9)
17 Goes on like a rural Cobbett (5)
19 Now competent enough to be introduced (11)
22 Bit of a tea-dance? (3)
23 Drama figure to be distinguished from Lear, etc. (7)
24 Carrying in one direction (7)
26 Position taken by a golfer (6)
27 He's initially identified on the road (7)

DOWN

1 Pointed entertainment in the amusement arcade (7)
2 Sailor's proposed marriage causing a fight? (5, 10)
3 Let on he's deadly! (3)
4 Light on something synthetic (5)
5 The old lady's jokes are just common sense (6-3)
6 Sound rather slow as a talker (5)
7 To be expected when the orchestra decided to do something? (9, 6)
8 Small creature employed with crushing effect (6)
12 Is a man able to provide navigation? (5)
14 Dream of Black Bess? (9)
15 Concede a colour may be short (5)
16 He weakens the enemy (6)
18 Cause astonishment with faulty footwork (7)
20 Personally disposed of (5)
21 Ill-advised build-up of foreign talks (5)
25 She carries the can in the country (3)

96

ACROSS

1 They require patient obedience (7, 6)
8 As it's half-time let's have a drink! (4)
9 Irishman returns a hit (3)
10 Talk with a gravity that disturbs Alice (6)
11 Hurry to take instruction where fancies have a price (10)
13 Young girl endlessly seen as an assistant (4)
14 Spirit of the city (6)
16 Cause confusion with incitement to greater abandon (8)
19 He takes a shine to what the craftsman's made (8)
22 Some monster spilling gore on the ship (6)
25 He gets a bit rough fighting villains (4)
26 Top quality joint belonging to the man in front (10)
27 Element of misplaced aid in drink (6)
28 Current mover possibly electric (3)
29 Operates at different levels (4)
30 Having an illuminating touch of dishonesty? (5-8)

DOWN

1 Possibly catching something uncomfortable (7)
2 Feature bearing of a foreigner (7)
3 He might be able to set right a shot poet (9)
4 Way to work a concession (3)
5 Not to be trusted if not one of the herd (5)
6 Advice to a golfer to have vision (7)
7 Revolution misled at a turning-point (7)
12 Female art bore making a new arrangement (7)
15 Turn in fifty with nothing to show for it (3)
17 Long John's insensitive supporter (6, 3)
18 Expected to arrive for payment (3)
20 As worn by the worker at the top? (7)
21 Making a smooth impression (7)
23 His stock-taking isn't entirely unsound (7)
24 Got a whiff of something one disapproved (7)
26 Thus far and no farther! (5)
28 Priest of the Carmelite order (3)

97

ACROSS

1 Best vessel in the competition? (12)
8 Witty about crime in a clothes shop (7)
9 Two vehicles to catch a small creature (3-4)
11 He takes a heavenly view of your prospects (10)
12 Almost uncanny visitors to the stable (4)
14 Music adding nothing to the performance (8)
16 There may be cross references to them in correspondence (6)
17 No great performer in amateur radio (3)
19 Valuable information about the aged (6)
21 Play it for kicks (8)
24 This voice makes a lot of difference (4)
25 Belonging to the colonel's command (10)
27 Bad painting said to provide an opening to Crosby (7)
28 Don't do it if you see a tar mark (7)
29 Great occasion when we heard from Moscow? (3-6, 3)

DOWN

1 Punish a small prince before time (7)
2 It tells us how hard the blow is (10)
3 Port brother? (8)
4 Compensation for the printer (6)
5 Island in the blue we hear (4)
6 Are they made by attackers with no thought of retreat? (7)
7 Troops to protect the loan? (7, 5)
10 Does it indicate when there's a full load of footwear aboard? (8, 4)
13 Unhappy enough to have expired with inner strain (10)
15 The lout has taken a slice off the top! (3)
18 Giving Tim a vote might possibly provide a reason (8)
20 Suggestion that we go into the salad-bowl it may be said (7)
22 He knows what our chances of survival are (7)
23 Adjust the wig if it's a burden (6)
26 Drink it till you're topped up (4)

98

ACROSS

6 A little gold for the semi-royal personage? (4, 1, 9)
9 Service conductor (6)
10 Signs of not being at one but still getting on (8)
11 One of the cases lost at Boston (3-5)
13 Anticipate a delivery (6)
15 Suit and pumps (6)
17 Meets with a reverse after Edward starts to show respect (6)
19 Aspire to be different in the country (6)
20 Foreign people I found in an island (8)
22 It may be made with engaging intent (8)
24 Before getting in row back for the sea nymph (6)
26 Bonny Prince giving a man nothing back — that's comic! (7, 7)

DOWN

1 To demand global payment is excessive (6, 3, 5)
2 It might make matters rather sticky (4)
3 Frighten with something noisy? (6)
4 They're fine when one's dressing up (8)
5 Be a good chap, that's most satisfactory! (4)
7 Flamboyant talk about giving Napoleon his head (6)
8 Great chums of Priestley's (4, 10)
12 In which one might learn social status? (5)
14 Pride oneself on one's feathers? (5)
16 Send St. Martin the wrong way (8)
18 Inclined to be bitter in the French manner? (6)
21 Mr. Grundy's birthday (6)
23 Drink welcome in a great petrol storm (4)
25 Part of an enterprise (4)

99

ACROSS

1 Opening supporter (8)
5 Capital doctor on the boat (6)
9 A water-colour? (8)
10 Clergyman back with the Frenchman's refusal to give a name (6)
12 One front is the Russian (4)
13 Not very good speed after the first time? (6-4)
15 Building coloured by a royal family? (5, 2, 6)
19 A sucker for dirty carpets (6-7)
23 The one that does the dialling? (4-6)
25 Where one may have an attachment to breeding? (4)
28 He's versed in making a name for himself (6)
29 One might give a girl a hand for it (8)
30 Measures across (6)
31 Delightful if we can follow the bad road (8)

DOWN

1 Pigs so strange must cause talk! (6)
2 Brilliance of a lady's head (5)
3 Get ready to go for cards (4)
4 Super manoeuvre to join me at the top! (7)
6 Nymph in the mineral poster (5)
7 It holds something that might have been in art once (9)
8 The man from Wolverhampton? (8)
11 Give fifty to the fool for bread (4)
14 Twice she takes a politician from the mass (4)
15 Stale as an old cab? (9)
16 Liquid power (3)
17 Very bad line-up (4)
18 Presented an exaggerated picture of one's financial position? (8)
20 Able to start eating something sugary (4)
21 Gem of an isle, Ireland! (7)
22 Stick at this time and place (6)
24 In which one makes a personal appearance (5)
26 It's up for approval (5)
27 The unbelievable Billy! (4)

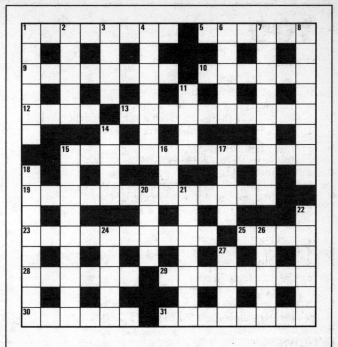

100

ACROSS

1 The first conqueror (4, 7)
9 Put out by going into the wrong dive, etc. (7)
10 Peter accepting discomfort in fine style (7)
11 One of those things on which a ring may depend (3)
12 He learns to take a short break after science and before that endless art (7)
13 Grave summing-up on departure (7)
14 Tea number (3)
15 One might pick it up to move faster (5)
17 No girl comes back for this material (5)
18 The French have a word for it and set it to music (5)
20 Silly Cyril's song (5)
22 Theologian might put more on (3)
24 Get me in abounding trouble (7)
25 React like a shaken man (7)
26 The way some like it (3)
27 He doesn't live in a dream world (7)
28 Having no experience of legal defence? (7)
29 Her Paris elopement led to war (5, 2, 4)

DOWN

1 Is he clean as well as chivalrous? (6, 2, 3, 4)
2 It might be rash to touch them (7)
3 Like a broad river only more so (5)
4 He sees what one's saying (3-6)
5 Hang-up for the drinking man (3-4)
6 Time for a girl to appear in the garden (10, 5)
7 No difficulty in the race for service (3-3)
8 One female bird just like another? (6)
16 Two points reduce the burden of ignorance (9)
18 Covering the river when fully grown (6)
19 Test about half a dozen of no importance (7)
21 Going against the business table (7)
23 Scorn to give the German an incomplete idea (6)
25 Eat too much of the substance? (5)

101

ACROSS

1 Protection when getting ready for departure (7)
5 They're drawn at the end of the play (6)
9 Raise a girl in the middle (7)
10 Ice cult adapted for personal cover (7)
11 The literary man might dip into it (3)
12 It's taken to indicate one's state of health (11)
13 It might stick out of the ice (5)
14 Not in form? (9)
16 Every one is supposed to know simple facts (9)
17 Reach maturity without direction in a body (5)
19 Is he responsible for funny business in the basement? (3, 8)
22 Make a hit as a lace-maker (3)
23 Making arrangements for easier delivery (7)
24 Biblical mess (7)
26 Go up as cheering starts at last (6)
27 Graceful time for a child (7)

DOWN

1 It gives some a look-in before others (7)
2 Factory office employee looking after the building? (5, 2, 3, 5)
3 She's a bit of a harridan (3)
4 Make light of wild gale at Minehead (5)
5 Some sort of bird to take the letters (9)
6 Even more inclined to make a Marine blue (5)
7 Visionary message from a distant well-wisher (7, 8)
8 Break about an Anglican vessel (6)
12 Final pint or so going into the body (5)
14 Deems grub, perhaps, to have been sunk (9)
15 Man of marble (5)
16 Quite a disturbance when one hits the water! (6)
18 Try poet in a different craft (7)
20 Put a ring on the tree to provide a view (5)
21 It must affect the outcome (5)
25 Obligation to play the game? (3)

102

ACROSS

1 Combining both of Simon's qualities? (4, 3, 6)
8 A bit of a stickler for drink (4)
9 Show distress when the chief doesn't quite come back (3)
10 Where food is kept for one to put fat on? (6)
11 Quite wrongly Tim's arming the incomers (10)
13 Money for a jotting (4)
14 Faithless in fact (6)
16 Something cut with speed when table-tennis starts (8)
19 Always carrying on like the gods (8)
22 Possible danger from the Mad Hatter (6)
25 The charge is about right but you needn't pay it (4)
26 Festival of the erring Saint Laura (10)
27 Her sin being removed at a place of worship (6)
28 Bonneted fancy (3)
29 Feeling you get from that enemy propaganda (4)
30 Soldier taking the paper every day? (7, 6)

DOWN

1 He helps to ensure that you get the message (7)
2 One of the less sunny princes? (7)
3 Able to take in liquid (9)
4 Very good at swimming, bad at getting up (3)
5 The singer's road might lead to them (5)
6 Standard price bargain at the greengrocer's (7)
7 Always overweight for football (7)
12 Head supporter allowed to provide adornment (7)
15 He'll get beaten if he appears again! (3)
17 Put an oar in when it's not your row (9)
18 Man one might not entirely take to (3)
20 He demonstrates some brandy on the girl (7)
21 Starting a key activity (7)
23 Came to discomfort in debt (7)
24 An Italian way to eminence as a flier (7)
26 Time of enchantment (5)
28 Exclude a transaction with no profit (3)

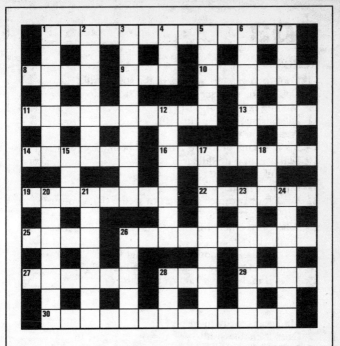

103

ACROSS

1 Fool to give a girl a share in the statement! (12)
8 Getting the message from town (7)
9 Moving talk about port (7)
11 Establishment of spirits (10)
12 Weapon in water (4)
14 It's not a major job to indicate a boundary (4-4)
16 Seal gets in a muddle (6)
17 A drink for Rose? (3)
19 Entrance money? (6)
21 Four-foot-two-inch fastener to secure the revolver (8)
24 Battery burner? (4)
25 Where one caters for the others with a high-class tirade (10)
27 It's usually kept under a lid at night (7)
28 Allure of Dorothy's sister Gloria, maybe? (7)
29 Does it make one afraid to park? (6, 6)

DOWN

1 Mad seas crazily piled up (7)
2 Does it enable you to see a ghost at night? (6-4)
3 Bad at living without missing anything (8)
4 Go on it with something quotable (6)
5 Most of the meat is solid wood! (4)
6 That's what you think! (7)
7 Pestered Tina as ordained earlier (12)
10 Hospitality from a shopkeeper? That'll be the day! (5, 2, 5)
13 Put off being brave? (10)
15 It streaks through the water (3)
18 Letting nothing in after drawing intoxicating breath? (8)
20 Features language of foreigners (7)
22 You'd be proud to be like one? (7)
23 Society chap (6)
26 Willie starts to be ill and complain (4)

104

ACROSS

6 The way to get to the point (4, 2, 8)
9 Think back about the thousand dollars given for a piece (6)
10 One of those at a Scottish gathering (8)
11 Telling renderings? (8)
13 Taking off the pressure when it's Angie's turn (6)
15 Sure to come round with me when we start again (6)
17 See the road turn when you take a walk (6)
19 Accommodation for the in-crowd (6)
20 He hopes to choose one before there's bad visibility (8)
22 Loyal sticker? (8)
24 Lawyers find a chap to provide refreshers (6)
26 Where a cash sale is not allowed? (5-5, 4)

DOWN

1 Sound ammunition but it won't kill anybody (5, 9)
2 Comfortable room in a pub (4)
3 Two-step city (6)
4 Their heir might be seen to be so (8)
5 Stirling not taken in by the Rolling Stones? (4)
7 Approach to do something about an island (6)
8 Conqueror's territory belonging to the conquered (7, 7)
12 Look here for a caravan camp (5)
14 Disturbance in the West End or Maidenhead (5)
16 Painter chap with the wrong agent (8)
18 Don city (6)
21 Heraldic form of bad art (6)
23 Odd man out of the team with the Spanish missing? (4)
25 No doubt about a pound (4)

105

ACROSS

1 Crazy hopper in a solo dance (8)
5 One taking steps to provide entertainment (6)
9 Wise about boat damage done by the resistance (8)
10 Music man making a connection in Georgia (6)
12 At 51 no carpets — it's laid down (4)
13 Strange figures make requests go astray (10)
15 Not what you'd expect to hear from sly mountain folk? (5-8)
19 Where one might be in a position to blast off (9, 4)
23 Don't let Heather fly, the common person! (10)
25 You may put your foot in it (4)
28 Get ahead fast in this (6)
29 Striking creature hanging from a tree? (5-3)
30 They add something to the crowd scenes (6)
31 He has a withering effect, the wretch! (8)

DOWN

1 Be quick to put the pressure on (6)
2 Day on TV (5)
3 Feeling for the unfortunate (4)
4 Beastly club bars? (3-4)
6 It shows where a salt might have moved around (5)
7 No nice cub is found living in sin (9)
8 Provider of moving advice or instruction (4, 4)
11 It may be taken to advance one's standing (4)
14 Powder taken in total confidence (4)
15 Rich ruler of the underworld? (9)
16 Up very early every morning (3)
17 African leader for a short time (4)
18 Supporter of national display (4-4)
20 Church walk not starting when there's water around (4)
21 Not particular in this (7)
22 No do-it-yourself in the phone book so he provides services (6)
24 Is Latin found in North America, girl? (5)
26 It's customary for riding (5)
27 Flight supporter (4)

106

ACROSS

1 A call Aramis might make as a singer (5, 6)
9 Smuggle grain into town (7)
10 Regret that some err badly (7)
11 After half a century he'll show a resemblance (3)
12 Centre of a dance revolution (7)
13 Given money that at last was due (7)
14 I myself, for instance, take nothing (3)
15 It counteracts the effect of a ladder (5)
17 A change of rig seems to me to show the dirt (5)
18 Ed's left sleeping space for the sweeper (5)
20 Start to foresee a caper (5)
22 He's on his own (3)
24 Notes on wild dance rhythm (7)
25 Do they demonstrate how you might get wet? (7)
26 Came across in the opera house briefly (3)
27 Unholy lying about a sports body (7)
28 Key job at the start (7)
29 Is it expandable to include more musicians? (7, 4)

DOWN

1 Easy profit on second-hand cordage? (5, 3, 3, 4)
2 Causing trouble by giving the port to us (7)
3 She may have a wrong number (5)
4 Ten meagre turns expected from a yes-man (9)
5 It may need help over a stile (4, 3)
6 Indications that hats can be blown off? (6, 2, 3, 4)
7 Measure finding favour in the future scheme of things (6)
8 Sell on a bicycle, one hears (6)
16 Humiliation of a lowly dwelling? (9)
18 Manifestation of armed power (6)
19 Not a man disturbed in the state (7)
21 Affliction of a hundred at holiday time (7)
23 Plan to show how the thing ought to look (6)
25 West End officer in charge showing no emotion (5)

107

ACROSS

1 Having got the label shall we display the pills? (7)
5 Dog of an outcast! (6)
9 Tying up of a vessel in a way (7)
10 Going round the outer path (7)
11 Eminence in store (3)
12 Flower of sugar grass? (6-5)
13 Little Albert frequently seen up there (5)
14 Study the instruction programme at assembly (9)
16 An underground elf, one hears, could be marking time (9)
17 Cop it in a way that might cause talk (5)
19 Subject of Falstaff's final babble (5, 6)
22 After this, Dan, go for a dance (3)
23 He goes places on holiday (7)
24 When there's poison around, she's one to shriek (7)
26 Quiet hen in the team (6)
27 Came down not very heavily? (7)

DOWN

1 She is grateful for the part that gives a laugh (7)
2 Warning to trespassers — or recruits at the Guards depot? (6, 2, 3, 4)
3 Indelicate person (3)
4 The girl got a degree in the old country (5)
5 Just say the word! (9)
6 Garments that make Peter French look revolutionary (5)
7 Given a pretext by carelessness with millinery? (2, 3, 4, 2, 1, 3)
8 Happy as a spirited skylark? (6)
12 Cat turning up to suggest a saying (5)
14 He produces notes from a rich store (9)
15 One may swear to give them a hearing (5)
16 Powerful high? (6)
18 Struggle for a point of view (7)
20 In New York nothing is creating a racket (5)
21 After fifty a man achieves identification (5)
25 A horse can be a nuisance (3)

108

ACROSS

1 Do they enable one to see the stones? (6, 7)
8 Outstanding leader of men (4)
9 Drink when there's coldness in the air (3)
10 Look as if the hit will be diverting (6)
11 He's got it all! (10)
13 Does he make sure the comic doesn't starve? (4)
14 Man to take a pub on? No thanks! (6)
16 Excitement of a hanging? (8)
19 Business of the local chamber (8)
22 You don't get such income for nothing! (6)
25 Move around to cause a mix-up (4)
26 Lost blood with dagger twisted inside — it looks dirty! (10)
27 Let's give the commander our flag! (6)
28 Like a fellow of a benevolent society (3)
29 Many took sustenance after time (4)
30 Frightful time (5, 2, 6)

DOWN

1 Put in a better position to organise (7)
2 Graduates shortly to provide music (7)
3 Noel drawn as a man of property (9)
4 It shows something's missing (3)
5 Anything obtainable from Pharaoh's daughter (5)
6 Craftily acquire a bit of harness (7)
7 You'll do well to achieve it! (7)
12 Ten said to be provided as a substitute (7)
15 Funny sort of spirit! (3)
17 Marked half to be put in the rider's seat to make a getaway (9)
18 Woman with no things to say (3)
20 Move to become gliding champion? (7)
21 Polo personality turning in an inventor (7)
23 Soldier able to mark time? (7)
24 The only democrat in Hanover? (7)
26 Is it only a peer who can have beef nowadays? (5)
28 He hasn't got full use of his head, the idiot! (3)

109

ACROSS

1 The sort of transactions money makes bearable? (4, 3, 5)
8 Gets to grips with a management problem? (7)
9 Fit for the taking? (7)
11 He may help us to progress along certain lines (10)
12 In church, poor creatures (4)
14 House building site in the old country? (8)
16 Said to express coolness in decoration (6)
17 Immortal cause of the pet's return (3)
19 He takes a bow to begin his performance (6)
21 Competes in an eliminator with the top weight handicap (8)
24 Be quick to draw the line (4)
25 Should a tin look so strange? (10)
27 Most likely to be in touch (7)
28 Our dean can compose poetry (7)
29 Values may look different after this (12)

DOWN

1 Make sure you can fool the company (7)
2 Obstinate enough to have written a do-it-yourself testament? (4-6)
3 Weighing up the proverbial value? (8)
4 Consternation caused if one were to cancel permission? (6)
5 Part of the Hungarian Rhapsody can be sung (4)
6 Usual procedure for marking exit and entrance among engineers (7)
7 Official pipe? (12)
10 Almost too late for refreshment? (8, 4)
13 Source of a non-starter in the South of France (10)
15 Note sounding like American money (3)
18 Says it takes a month to get change in Aries (8)
20 Downfall of bad man in trial (7)
22 Easy to see I have come up to make an impression! (7)
23 Bustle in cunning fashion (6)
26 Middlesbrough is on this side (4)

110

ACROSS

6 Revolutionary way of getting tight? (4, 2, 3, 5)
9 Overdrawn and debts as well — that's nasty! (6)
10 Steer Ivy into showing some hardness (8)
11 Talk about deceptive doggerel! (8)
13 Man in the street going to Piccadilly Circus? (6)
15 Make the gun harmless to achieve a lighter effect (6)
17 Make the agent take things in again (6)
19 Gradual movement to making smoking less harmful (6)
20 It's not quite the same thing (8)
22 One lantern can be changed inside (8)
24 Cut down the distribution of crude on the way (6)
26 Very old chap found in a cave (11, 3)

DOWN

1 Group listening to the artists? (6 ,8)
2 Give the railways ten for spirit (4)
3 Cat landing us in more trouble (6)
4 Poetically contrary? (8)
5 A man loses nothing to make a mark (4)
7 Trying chap to have in the bedroom? (6)
8 There seems no prospect of another blow-out here (7, 7)
12 Little Virginia is allowed to be a servant (5)
14 Very good at identifying Alfred (5)
16 Drag near so as to be set (8)
18 Charm an animal into the back of a boat (6)
21 Round the globe river in Devon (6)
23 Unsaintly man to give you the bird! (4)
25 One building feature will be enough as far as I'm concerned! (4)

111

ACROSS

1 Hanger-on in an airborne troops position? (8)
5 Takes on a different post after making a small announcement (6)
9 Means of conveying a stiff greeting? (8)
10 Flag girl in nationalised industry (6)
12 A London Symphony Orchestra presentation too! (4)
13 Affliction of a long call (10)
15 Pressure on one's honour when money's tight? (6, 7)
19 Happiness of having a servant in the home? (8, 5)
23 Tough girl administering medieval torture (4, 6)
25 Firm with the old lady in a trance (4)
28 Escaper from a bad regime (6)
29 Top for smoothness though his manner may be rough (8)
30 Coming out with a familiar utterance (6)
31 He boasts of reading the rotten paper both ways inside (8)

DOWN

1 Liked to be heartless in the forest, perhaps (6)
2 Bloomers in a luxury bed (5)
3 Dismiss such poor cloth (4)
4 Railway travellers sometimes attain these ends (7)
6 Drink goes to Auntie's head causing excitement (5)
7 Writers about rivers haven't made any money (9)
8 We don't know who he is (8)
11 A girl to avoid (4)
14 Girl set up with old Bob (4)
15 Something to sell at a price (9)
16 Movement by a Roman when amorous (3)
17 A bit of ammunition is one thing (4)
18 They think the girl's great! (8)
20 Something missing from the Irish flag (4)
21 Wave of destruction? (7)
22 Outlaw group who have it (6)
24 Maureen shortly meets a man who's feeble-minded (5)
26 Entertainment during work time (5)
27 Put weapons up and be comfortable (4)

112

ACROSS

1 Thumping row among the sleepers? (6-5)
9 Moved fast in a different gear to settle matters (7)
10 Something wrong with me in faulty Latin (7)
11 Covering Rugby Union at Gateshead (3)
12 Confiscate each set that isn't properly assembled (7)
13 Creature providing a hot meal (7)
14 Second person to start a youth club (3)
15 Material reason for the dress being creased? (5)
17 Millinery to start queueing for (5)
18 After Branston it goes for a Burton (5)
20 Vision of engineers in a construction job (5)
22 It grows among the Michaelmas daisies (3)
24 Mostly in a big way? (7)
25 Mark the place to start from (7)
26 Snake round a woman's neck (3)
27 Put the enterprise on a higher level? (7)
28 Where Tania might gain a lot of ground in North Africa (7)
29 Project sporting news that will have some effect? (4, 7)

DOWN

1 Their dropping in might be unwelcome (9, 6)
2 Stays to invest a thousand dollars in shipping (7)
3 Nothing green can easily be seen (5)
4 Scent of paper in a foreign country (9)
5 Brave enough to please the ladies (7)
6 Game score requiring numerous replies (6, 9)
7 Linen for the neck? (6)
8 Fail to achieve an adequate intake (6)
16 Musical picnicker (5-4)
18 Flowers for a union with a kissing couple (6)
19 Lot more shaky in the music (7)
21 Fighting to spoil a twisted tail (7)
23 The cloth spends very little time with the fuzz (6)
25 Provides more than enough for the South African set-up (5)

113

ACROSS

1 Give the fellow reduced terms for part of the book (7)
5 Come to the point (6)
9 Had a top time (7)
10 Put in to simmer badly up to a point (7)
11 Time to count the years (3)
12 Expert calling that might arouse anger! (11)
13 Shout on the phone briefly for accommodation (5)
14 He's doing something deceptive with railroad tickets (9)
16 Ungodly quality (9)
17 Ground for making a name globally (5)
19 Incite Freud to be different without being thought mad (11)
22 Hospitality is in one's keeping (3)
23 Not many within one's grasp (7)
24 Prefer about fifty — but it's a matter of taste (7)
26 Such men are collared in a roundabout way (6)
27 Passed on a song in the plant (7)

DOWN

1 Drive clean away from it (3, 4)
2 Internal food movement system (10, 5)
3 Brown may have a go at a dance (3)
4 Do air turn to entertain (5)
5 No amity is available in this arrangement (9)
6 Drink to a degree that makes one dance (5)
7 Where there are still some innocent girls? (6, 9)
8 Familiar note offering points in a rent adjustment (6)
12 Friend and parent in a holiday spot (5)
14 Nothing of importance can be put this way (9)
15 Sounds as if one might want to handle the dough (5)
16 Openings for a feeder (6)
18 Sound fear of the barbarian number (7)
20 Assign some of the preference shares (5)
21 Deduce some gen with a cipher (5)
25 You can have the lot for a couple of pounds! (3)

114

ACROSS

1 Never ceasing to move with the times? (5, 3, 5)
8 Not new to exploitation (4)
9 Reserve container (3)
10 Having value on the lower deck (6)
11 Arrives first and takes back a portion the French can eat (10)
13 Minor prophet claiming to be great (4)
14 I'm first in grammar (6)
16 Lies self-injured seeming dead (8)
19 Score two short for a majority (8)
22 Morning cover in which one might be caught (6)
25 Number one personality (4)
26 Congress body (5, 5)
27 Horse from the dock? (6)
28 Abel makes her a different girl (3)
29 Help many inside to be sour (4)
30 Repeat part of the course (6, 7)

DOWN

1 Put back to bed with a mineral (7)
2 Take the cover off (7)
3 She's coming out this year (9)
4 The creature's back in Surrey! (3)
5 Cut up a number in custody (5)
6 Trip away from home as a means of escape? (7)
7 County relatives taking part of another one (7)
12 One girl could be another (7)
15 Not much to wear out it's fun! (3)
17 Such greetings, brother! (9)
18 Some of them usually can find you a bird (3)
20 Undercover venue for some sort of games (7)
21 Many in heroic chaos that suggests an epic (7)
23 Al being knocked about as an Asian (7)
24 Coming down to give you the drift, perhaps (7)
26 It might be brought up to scratch (5)
28 It's down in the forest (3)

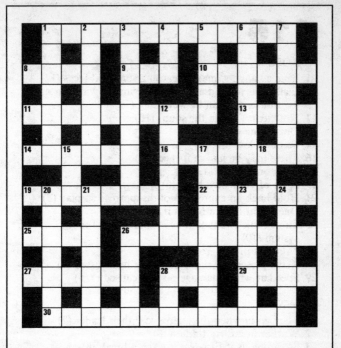

115

ACROSS

1 Irma's bangers, maybe, causing some red faces (12)
8 Jack turns and administers punishment with canes (7)
9 To snub a girl can be wounding (7)
11 Not clear if it's in the soup? (10)
12 Only some water? (4)
14 Scene of low life? (8)
16 There may be jam in its neck (6)
17 Pitch on the road (3)
19 A bit of your own back (6)
21 Hold back an expression of disapproval in play (8)
24 One might have a file on it (4)
25 Limit cable circulation as in some sort of money system (10)
27 Take out of the ground (7)
28 Artist presenting figures that can be assessed (7)
29 Speed at which damage may be caused (7, 5)

DOWN

1 They go in when the guards lose their leader (7)
2 Worker in a dirty trade? (10)
3 Sounding as if Erna's not given a break (8)
4 It may be put on at moments of stress (6)
5 The place you say you can see (4)
6 To dine in the home is most cleverly arranged (7)
7 In favour of Spud breaking the cane when there's swelling (12)
10 Ship's company on very short rations? (8, 4)
13 Port authority to cut the teacher's pay? (4-6)
15 Where one might get a drink for dancing? (3)
18 Have another look in the laboratory perhaps (8)
20 Show hostility when there's a brush (7)
22 He provides a service for the server (4-3)
23 Little beast providing equipment on time (6)
26 Just gathering? (4)

116

ACROSS

6 Arrival and departure no problem — that's the big spender's attitude (4, 4, 4, 2)
9 Prince on watch (6)
10 Agricultural red (8)
11 One doesn't like to pronounce it (8)
13 Deprived of a note in the head's cover (6)
15 Instrument of primitive reckoning (6)
17 He gives guidance on the motorway (6)
19 King of the Murphies (6)
20 Firing to get things moving? (8)
22 Where Queen Victoria took cover? (8)
24 Instructed to sound tight (6)
26 Is it given by the listener sitting beside you? (5, 9)

DOWN

1 Refuse, then come to grief? (7, 3, 4)
2 A chap who may seem different (4)
3 The mower had it in hand (6)
4 Time to reformulate one's creed about an award (8)
5 Exploiter of the striped trousered kind (4)
7 For keeping the crowd in order? Quite the contrary! (3-3)
8 Worthless in spite of unpaid virtue (4-3-7)
12 Glitter at the top (5)
14 Clinch with a hammering (5)
16 Perform inadequately as a bird covered by the carpet? (8)
18 Take away the bones for the band (6)
21 Recording an absence of metal gravity (6)
23 It causes a hold-up in sailing (4)
25 One thing for the counter (4)

117

ACROSS

1 The drawback with the grand dress is where to keep it (8)
5 Bill going round to the motorway showing such energy! (6)
9 By no means simple enclosure (8)
10 Writer given credit for going on in (6)
12 Scene of an occasional blow-out in Sicily (4)
13 Where one's fancy, it's hoped, has winning ways (10)
15 Tough cover for the grub (7-6)
19 In which electricity resources dictate the course of government? (5, 8)
23 Treat actor as material for a statue maybe (10)
25 Possibly a performer in a very small way (4)
28 Supervisor losing the right to be an enemy (6)
29 Figure there's a third party involved (8)
30 More than fifty join a ruler in affection (6)
31 Not an original performer (8)

DOWN

1 The work of making a basket (6)
2 Such a nose the old chap had! (5)
3 It's nonsense about one being in trouble (4)
4 Under the big fellow heat's been diverted (7)
6 Trunk in the boot or sometimes on the back seat (5)
7 Plants a chap on the birds (9)
8 Composition adding nothing to performance (8)
11 Heartless man who has been ennobled (4)
14 Couple with the quiet manner (4)
15 Find Jack at this level (5, 4)
16 Swimmer putting a shelter up (3)
17 Much may turn on where a mark is (4)
18 Malicious as fuel tips up (8)
20 Music-maker taking heart from American tramps (4)
21 One term in turmoil between events (7)
22 One may pursue it all one's working life (6)
24 A state briefly to take in once more (5)
26 Come down on a beam? (5)
27 Bit of a performance (4)

118

ACROSS

1 In which the business is all tied up? (7, 4)
9 Transport at the wrong rate for entertainment (7)
10 Comes out and gets together at one point (7)
11 It's taken in hand when there's a row (3)
12 Number one trend brought back for publication (7)
13 Girl set to be tough on the meat-eater (7)
14 Spoil a boy without money (3)
15 It causes quite a ferment (5)
17 Fun with fuel around the Middle East (5)
18 Let a pound reach a depressed level (5)
20 The old coin seems a bit of a dud to Tom (5)
22 It may be potted for a meal (3)
24 Sort of loaf at home? (7)
25 Vessel of some weight on the ring (7)
26 She's come to a big conclusion (3)
27 One way politicians get into the papers (7)
28 Survival is a matter of calculation to him (7)
29 In which traffic may play a dramatic part? (6, 5)

DOWN

1 Known family connections of a certain persuasion? (6, 9)
2 Make sure of complying with insane procedure? (7)
3 To the west of it is quite another place (5)
4 Like the busy Mr. Benn? (9)
5 Levelling out after the day's ups and downs? (7)
6 On which the law permits one to act? (10, 5)
7 How funny in a horror film! (6)
8 Weigh up tools on the way (6)
16 He's got it coming to him (9)
18 Something to be gained by entering (6)
19 More like Willie? (7)
21 He deals with other people's property (7)
23 Orders an artist to rise above the lights (6)
25 Category of instruction (5)

SOLUTIONS

PUZZLE No. 1

Across: 1, Public opinion. 8, Scot. 9, Dub. 10, Pastry. 11, Night-light. 13, Deal. 14, Citron. 16, Infernal. 19, Keep left. 22, Rubber. 25, Mess. 26, Portsmouth. 27, Invite. 28, Boa. 29, Ivan. 30, Rogues' gallery.

Down: 1, Puccini. 2, Butcher. 3, Indolence. 4, Orb. 5, Input. 6, Insider. 7, Nirvana. 12, Glitter. 15, Tie. 17, Forestall. 18, Nib. 20, Eleanor. 21, Passing. 23, Bromide. 24, Estuary. 26, Piece. 28, Bag.

PUZZLE No. 2

Across: 1, Sleeping pill. 8, Initial. 9, Delight. 11, Reanimated. 12, Blur. 14, Passages. 16, Play up. 17, Rap. 19, Target. 21, Domicile. 24, Boil. 25, Amanuensis. 27, Embargo. 28, Amateur. 29, Swing the lead.

Down: 1, Spirals. 2, Eliminates. 3, Pillager. 4, Nudges. 5, Pole. 6, Legally. 7, Disreputable. 10, Tyre pressure. 13, Illiterate. 15, Sad. 18, Poundage. 20, Rainbow. 22, Instead. 23, Import. 26, Bran.

PUZZLE No. 3

Across: 6, Room for dispute. 9, Amalfi. 10, Beefcake. 11, Pitchers. 13, Impair. 15, Emblem. 17, Relief. 19, Dollop. 20, Effusion. 22, Distrait. 24, Bertha. 26, Rear-view mirror.

Down: 1, From side to side. 2, Wool. 3, Office. 4, Fireside. 5, Epic. 7, Robust. 8, Take it from Here. 12, Cabal. 14, Plies. 16, Emphatic. 18, Bestow. 21, Fabric. 23, Turn. 25, Rare.

PUZZLE No. 4

Across: 1, Columbus. 5, Chaste. 9, Divinity. 10, Ballad. 12, Earl. 13, Mind-reader. 15, Sounding-board. 19, Pair of glasses. 23, Cadaverous. 25, Fair. 28, Mainly. 29, Ribaldry. 30, Nether. 31, Decanter.

Down: 1, Codger. 2, Liver. 3, Mink. 4, Untried. 6, Heave. 7, Salad days. 8, El dorado. 11, Eden. 14, Juno. 15, Spindrift. 16, Ill. 17, Bosh. 18, Specimen. 20, Garb. 21, Abusive. 22, Prayer. 24, Value. 26, Audit. 27, Gala.

PUZZLE No. 5

Across: 1, Belly-dancer. 9, Closure. 10, Trainer. 11, Lie. 12, Muddied. 13, Railway. 14, Inn. 15, Hippo. 17, Toyed. 18, Mates. 20, Ranch. 22, All. 24, Counter. 25, Desired. 26, Ice. 27, Widened. 28, Brigade. 29, Rocket-range.

Down: 1, Blood-and-thunder. 2, Loutish. 3, Yield. 4, Afternoon. 5, Chariot. 6, Runaway marriage. 7, Scampi. 8, Frayed. 16, Partridge. 18, Macaws. 19, Satanic. 21, Hessian. 23, Lodger. 25, Debar.

PUZZLE No. 6

Across: 1, Noodles. 5, Puddle. 9, Nodders. 10, Expense. 11, Tor. 12, Conventions. 13, Payee. 14, Pre-

vented. 16, Shortfall. 17, Views. 19, Impositions. 22, Ida. 23, Erratic. 24, Kipling. 26, Floral. 27, Manager.
Down: 1, Non-stop. 2, Orderly corporal. 3, Lee. 4, Susan. 5, Piecemeal. 6, Depot. 7, Land of the living. 8, Leased. 12, Chest. 14, Practical. 15, Elves. 16, Spider. 18, Swagger. 20, Satyr. 21, Oakum. 25, Pin.

PUZZLE No. 7

Across: 1, Dead-reckoning. 8, Asia. 9, Sow. 10, Divert. 11, Commandeer. 13, Diet. 14, Hendon. 16, Decorate. 19, Muleteer. 22, Nectar. 25, Idea. 26, Prevailing. 27, Setter. 28, Bin. 29, Bite. 30, Secret Service.
Down: 1, Dispose. 2, Alarmed. 3, Resonance. 4, Cow. 5, Order. 6, Invader. 7, Garment. 12, Endorse. 15, Nil. 17, Container. 18, Apt. 20, Undress. 21, Elastic. 23, Colibri. 24, Annette. 26, Purse. 28, Bus.

PUZZLE No. 8

Across: 1, Subsequently. 8, Looting. 9, Impious. 11, Cogitation. 12, Zinc. 14, Observer. 16, Demean. 17, Nod. 19, Facing. 21, Distrain. 24, Acre. 25, Contingent. 27, Sampler. 28, Noisier. 29, Electric blue.
Down: 1, Sponges. 2, Blistering. 3, Eighteen. 4, Unison. 5, Nape. 6, Leonine. 7, Block of flats. 10, Second nature. 13, Centennial. 15, Rod. 18, Diatonic. 20, Caramel. 22, Ape-like. 23, Horror. 26, Alec.

PUZZLE No. 9

Across: 6, Reflected glory. 9, Unused. 10, Acquaint. 11, Vestment. 13, Afraid. 15, Humble. 17, Seeing. 19, Crayon. 20, Tampered. 22, Singular. 24, Spread. 26, Agreed to differ.
Down: 1, Prince Charming. 2, Efts. 3, Meddle. 4, Adequate. 5, Flea. 7, Traits. 8, Running repairs. 12, Tommy. 14, Rhine. 16, Landlady.

18, Stereo. 21, Mystic. 23, Glen. 25, Rife.

PUZZLE No. 10

Across: 1, Cupboard. 5, Washes. 9, Converge. 10, Hostel. 12, Luck. 13, Attainment. 15, Bargain hunter. 19, Treat like dirt. 23, Take notice. 25, Stop. 28, Hoards. 29, Moderate. 30, Sitter. 31, Searcher.
Down: 1, Cockle. 2, Panic. 3, Open. 4, Regatta. 6, Acorn. 7, Hottentot. 8, Salutary. 11, Pain. 14, Fret. 15, Breakfast. 16, Ink. 17, Unit. 18, Stitches. 20, Iota. 21, Enclose. 22, Appear. 24, Nudge. 26, Trash. 27, Bear.

PUZZLE No. 11

Across: 1, Bank balance. 9, Treacle. 10, Berserk. 11, Are. 12, Trailed. 13, Rooster. 14, Sad. 15, Extol. 17, Knots. 18, Ankle. 20, Noyes. 22, Arc. 24, Cottage. 25, Leander. 26, Ray. 27, Related. 28, Respect. 29, Second-class.
Down: 1, Beer and skittles. 2, Nacelle. 3, Bread. 4, Liberally. 5, Norfolk. 6, Election address. 7, Status. 8, Skirts. 16, Tenterden. 18, Accord. 19, Elastic. 21, Swansea. 23, Curate. 25, Lyric.

PUZZLE No. 12

Across: 1, Deficit. 5, Desire. 9, Solomon. 10, Parasol. 11, Aid. 12, Contraption. 13, Dream. 14, Mountings. 16, Desecrate. 17, Irons. 19, Overbidding. 22, Lob. 23, Amateur. 24, Legatee. 26, Tended. 27, Tempest.
Down: 1, Disband. 2, Full-dress debate. 3, Cam. 4, Tenon. 5, Departure. 6, Strap. 7, Russian roulette. 8, Planks. 12, Comic. 14, Meandered. 15, Thing. 16, Deodar. 18, Subject. 20, Bread. 21, Islet. 25, Gum.

PUZZLE No. 13

Across: 1, Parrot fashion. 8, Trim. 9, Set. 10, Relict. 11, Wonderland. 13, Mild. 14, Stella. 16, Starched.

19, Daughter. 22, Better. 25, Stir. 26, Lederhosen. 27, Remain. 28, Bar. 29, Teak. 30, Spending spree. **Down:** 1, Purport. 2, Remodel. 3, Observant. 4, Fit. 5, Shred. 6, Islamic. 7, Nacelle. 12, Assured. 15, Emu. 17, Ambergris. 18, Hot. 20, Actress. 21, Germane. 23, Trotter. 24, Elevate. 26, Lined. 28, Bun.

PUZZLE No. 14

Across: 1, Skipping rope. 8, Arrival. 9, Rubbish. 11, Fractional. 12, Fair. 14, Rosettes. 16, Arrest. 17, Red. 19, Action. 21, Airstrip. 24, Ibis. 25, Stag-beetle. 27, Nothing. 28, Extorts. 29, Get plastered. **Down:** 1, Streaks. 2, Invitation. 3, Pullover. 4, Normal. 5, Ruby. 6, Private. 7, Malformation. 10, Hard to please. 13, Prospector. 15, Sea. 18, Dingiest. 20, Thistle. 22, Retired. 23, Stigma. 26, Lisp.

PUZZLE No. 15

Across: 6, Out of this world. 9, Sponge. 10, Aperture. 11, Intended. 13, Bottom. 15, Outfit. 17, Depart. 19, Spirit. 20, Absentee. 22, Temporal. 24, Repast. 26, Decimal coinage. **Down:** 1, Companion piece. 2, Eton. 3, Offend. 4, Assemble. 5, Bolt. 7, Hoards. 8, Lord of the Isles. 12, Enter. 14, Train. 16, Internal. 18, Gallic. 21, Strain. 23, Pain. 25, Plan.

PUZZLE No. 16

Across: 1, District. 5, Struts. 9, Seminary. 10, Coupon. 12, Ring. 13, Barometric. 15, Place of honour. 19, Rogue elephant. 23, Grandstand. 25, Scot. 28, Astray. 29, Quatrain. 30, Trying. 31, Intrepid. **Down:** 1, Desert. 2, Simon. 3, Rank. 4, Carnage. 6, Trove. 7, Uppermost. 8, Sinecure. 11, Wolf. 14, Safe. 15, Pageantry. 16, Ode. 17, Oban. 18, Braggart. 20, Lute. 21, Penguin. 22, Stoned. 24, Drain. 26, Cramp. 27, Stir.

PUZZLE No. 17

Across: 1, Bull and Bush. 9, Infancy. 10, Missile. 11, Sob. 12, Obtains. 13, Another. 14, Yea. 15, Grant. 17, Noose. 18, Audit. 20, Sonia. 22, Fee. 24, Pattern. 25, Accuser. 26, Apt. 27, Cartoon. 28, Toiling. 29, Smoke-screen. **Down:** 1, By fits and starts. 2, Landing. 3, Abyss. 4, Dumbarton. 5, Unsworn. 6, Height of fashion. 7, Simony. 8, Degree. 16, Assonance. 18, Aspect. 19, Tremolo. 21, Ascribe. 23, Enrage. 25, Attic.

PUZZLE No. 18

Across: 1, Dubious. 5, Topics. 9, Satiety. 10, Undergo. 11, Ado. 12, Overbalance. 13, Felon. 14, Peasantry. 16, Dispersal. 17, Aloes. 19, Experienced. 22, Rib. 23, Ear-ring. 24, October. 26, Meteor. 27, Swansea. **Down:** 1, Distaff. 2, Bottomless purse. 3, One. 4, Style. 5, Thumbnail. 6, Pedal. 7, Coronation robes. 8, Lovely. 12, Ounce. 14, Passenger. 15, Award. 16, Deepen. 18, Siberia. 20, Rhine. 21, Cross. 25, Tea.

PUZZLE No. 19

Across: 1, Trigger finger. 8, Apse. 9, Lap. 10, Lilian. 11, Contractor. 13, Laid. 14, Strait. 16, Newcomer. 19, Betrayer. 22, Isobar. 25, Less. 26, Collection. 27, Stumer. 28, Awl. 29, Ruth. 30, Red Riding Hood. **Down:** 1, Top-coat. 2, Inertia. 3, Gallantry. 4, Rip. 5, Idler. 6, Galileo. 7, Realise (or-ze). 12, Tendril. 15, Rat. 17, White flag. 18, Mob. 20, Erector. 21, Resumed. 23, Ontario. 24, Adopted. 26, Corgi. 28, Ali.

PUZZLE No. 20

Across: 1, Whipping-post. 8, Hateful. 9, Logical. 11, Inheriting. 12, Berg. 14, Streaker. 16, Dorset. 17, Sip. 19, Occult. 21, Promoter. 24,

Iris. 25, Dispensing. 27, Grenade. 28, Stamped. 29, Demonstrator.
Down: 1, Watcher. 2, Informally. 3, Palettes. 4, Nylons. 5, Page. 6, Success. 7, Chain-smoking. 10, Light Brigade. 13, Commandant. 15, Rip. 18, Proposer. 20, Chinese. 22, Tripper. 23, Divers. 26, Sago.

PUZZLE No. 21

Across: 6, Restore harmony. 9, Adored. 10, Exclaims. 11, Psaltery. 13, Collar. 15, Induce. 17, Fluted. 19, Carnal. 20, Innuendo. 22, Sillabub. 24, Gantry. 26, Investigations.
Down: 1, Predestination. 2, User. 3, Poodle. 4, Farcical. 5, Emma. 7, Evelyn. 8, Name and address. 12, Laden. 14, Lathe. 16, Celibate. 18, Kit-bag. 21, Nights. 23, Lien. 25, Nook.

PUZZLE No. 22

Across: 1, Bird-lime. 5, Scales. 9, Mulberry. 10, Cannon. 12, Lark. 13, Camberwell. 15, Sporting print. 19, Parliamentary. 23, Appreciate. 25, Ache. 28, Loiter. 29, Misnomer. 30, Digest. 31, Ignorant.
Down: 1, Bumble. 2, Ruler. 3, Leek. 4, Mordant. 6, Chair. 7, Longevity. 8, Senility. 11, Oban. 14, Gobi. 15, Stripling. 16, Ire. 17, Play. 18, Sprawled. 20, Mail. 21, Nothing. 22, Secret. 24, Evens. 26, Comma. 27, Undo.

PUZZLE No. 23

Across: 1, Still waters. 9, Ambling. 10, Rat-hole. 11, Hue. 12, Currant. 13, Emerged. 14, Don. 15, Emile. 17, Tenor. 18, Get-up. 20, Fatal. 22, Air. 24, Clobber. 25, Angered. 26, Mum. 27, Regalia. 28, Bravado. 29, Tommy Steele.
Down: 1, Sobering thought. 2, Imitate. 3, Light. 4, Agreement. 5, Entreat. 6, Shotgun marriage. 7, Rancid. 8, Lender. 16, Infirmary. 18, Go-cart. 19, Pabulum. 21, Luggage. 23, Radios. 25, Ambit.

PUZZLE No. 24

Across: 1, Bustard. 5, Sesame. 9, Trapper. 10, Slender. 11, Tar. 12, Inclination. 13, Bonus. 14, Britisher. 16, Nipperkin. 17, Dumas. 19, Garnishings. 22, Tab. 23, Tonneau. 24, Defence. 26, Breeze. 27, Egghead.
Down: 1, Bathtub. 2, Sparring partner. 3, Asp. 4, Doric. 5, Suspicion. 6, Sheba. 7, Midnight matinee. 8, Ironer. 12, Issue. 14, Bakehouse. 15, Indus. 16, Nights. 18, Subtend. 20, Irene. 21, Nudge. 25, Fig.

PUZZLE No. 25

Across: 1, Short and sweet. 8, Half. 9, Sap. 10, Agenda. 11, Foundation. 13, Neon. 14, Allege. 16, Surprise. 19, Attested. 22, Cheese. 25, Pact. 26, Shropshire. 27, Office. 28, Eli. 29, Lope. 30, Cheap and nasty.
Down: 1, Sea-coal. 2, Offence. 3, Testament. 4, Nap. 5, Spain. 6, Eleanor. 7, Tedious. 12, Insider. 15, Lot. 17, Reception. 18, Ice. 20, Traffic. 21, Entwine. 23, Exhales. 24, Scrappy. 26, Steep. 28, Eon.

PUZZLE No. 26

Across: 1, Unhesitating. 8, Intense. 9, Preview. 11, Hemisphere. 12, Thai. 14, Sediment. 16, Untrue. 17, Gas. 19, Unfold. 21, Pastiche. 24, Exam. 25, Ear-trumpet. 27, Eminent. 28, Astride. 29, Second course.
Down: 1, Untamed. 2, Handsomely. 3, Seething. 4, Tapers. 5, Tees. 6, Neither. 7, Tight squeeze. 10, White feather. 13, Instructor. 15, Tap. 18, Santiago. 20, Fragile. 22, Captive. 23, Parted. 26, Veto.

PUZZLE No. 27

Across: 6, Uninvited guest. 9, Spider. 10, Relation. 11, Timorous. 13, Tricky. 15, Exhume. 17, Writer. 19, Harris. 20, Immortal. 22, Skirting. 24, Dreamy. 26, Strip for action.

Down: 1, Surprise packet. 2, Wind. 3, Overdo. 4, Idolator. 5, Punt. 7, Thrush. 8, Shock treatment. 12, Other. 14, Inter. 16, Mastiffs. 18, Singer. 21, Medico. 23, Rain. 25, Exit.

PUZZLE No. 28

Across: 1, Dip-stick. 5, Wigwam. 9, Luminary. 10, Cannon. 12, Dash. 13, Vanity Fair. 15, Friendly match. 19, Traffic warden. 23, Authorised. 25, Cake. 28, Knotty. 29, Manifold. 30, Resort. 31, Leap-year.

Down: 1, Delude. 2, Pumps. 3, Tank. 4, Certain. 6, Italy. 7, Wincanton. 8, Monarchy. 11, Dial. 14, Biff. 15, Fractious. 16, Dew. 17, Mode. 18, Attacker. 20, Clip. 21, Average. 22, Leader. 24, Outer. 26, Abode. 27, Limp.

PUZZLE No. 29

Across: 1, Waiting-list. 9, Sniffle. 10, Echelon. 11, Pin. 12, Ballast. 13, Gordons. 14, Eon. 15, Esher. 17, Toted. 18, Dudes. 20, Style. 22, Odd. 24, Verbena. 25, Sailing. 26, Nut. 27, Deified. 28, Air-line. 29, Halcyon days.

Down: 1, Whirling Dervish. 2, Inflate. 3, Inept. 4, Glengarry. 5, Inherit. 6, Tale of Two Cities. 7, Usable. 8, Unused. 16, Husbandry. 18, Divide. 19, Special. 21, Eritrea. 23, Dogger. 25, Stain.

PUZZLE No. 30

Across: 1, Pea soup. 5, Sallow. 9, Outcast. 10, Radical. 11, Egg. 12, Hard-pressed. 13, Brawl. 14, Hailstone. 16, Schooling. 17, Plant. 19, Mountaineer. 22, Tan. 23, Intrude. 24, Slumber. 26, Orders. 27, Sunbeam.

Down: 1, Proverb. 2, Autograph hunter. 3, Ova. 4, Peter. 5, Stripling. 6, Lodge. 7, Occasional table. 8, Pledge. 12, Hello. 14, Hairiness. 15, Super. 16, Summit. 18, Tantrum. 20, Truce. 21, Eases. 25, Urn.

PUZZLE No. 31

Across: 1, Chain of office. 8, Slav. 9, Nag. 10, Elapse. 11, Transposed. 13, Ivan. 14, Demean. 16, Impinged. 19, Engineer. 22, Kissed. 25, Itch. 26, Depository. 27, Alumni. 28, Tea. 29, Item. 30, Ding-dong fight.

Down: 1, Calorie. 2, Advance. 3, Ninepence. 4, Fog. 5, Fiend. 6, Iranian. 7, Eustace. 12, Stirrup. 15, Mug. 17, Pikestaff. 18, Gas. 20, Nettled. 21, Inhuman. 23, Sitting. 24, Earnest. 26, Dried. 28, Ton.

PUZZLE No. 32

Across: 1, Pride of place. 8, Railcar. 9, Through. 11, Matterhorn. 12, King. 14, Sergeant. 16, Fierce. 17, God. 19, Detect. 21, Momentum. 24, Army. 25, Fare-paying. 27, Dilemma. 28, Tribute. 29, Frankincense.

Down: 1, Pointer. 2, Inclemency. 3, Earthing. 4, Future. 5, Lyre. 6, Courier. 7, Promised Land. 10, Hugger-mugger. 13, Liberation. 15, Tom. 18, Domestic. 20, Tumbler. 22, Tribune. 23, Malawi. 26, Omen.

PUZZLE No. 33

Across: 6, Hard nut to crack. 9, Pronto. 10, Nuthatch. 11, Academic. 13, Breath. 15, Evince. 17, Gemini. 19, Pastor. 20, Practise. 22, Stoppage. 24, Indian. 26, Criminal charge.

Down: 1, Character actor. 2, Grin. 3, Inform. 4, Portable. 5, Area. 7, Tenace. 8, Cocktail shaker. 12, Drift. 14, Edict. 16, Curtains. 18, Appeal. 21, Alight. 23, Puma. 25, Dark.

PUZZLE No. 34

Across: 1, Hesitate. 5, Campus. 9, Ministry. 10, Rococo. 12, Eden. 13, Medicament. 15, Period costume. 19, Mountain range. 23, Ordination. 25, Scar. 28, Thrill. 29, Derelict. 30, Rodent. 31, Eyebrows.

Down: 1, Hamper. 2, Singe. 3, Test. 4, Torpedo. 6, Aroma. 7, Procedure. 8, Short leg. 11, Disc. 14, Writ. 15, Plundered. 16, Don. 17, Sink. 18, Importer. 20, Iota. 21, Rookery. 22, Brutus. 24, Nylon. 26, Cairo. 27, Herb.

PUZZLE No. 35

Across: 1, Pull strings. 9, Profuse. 10, Torment. 11, Nut. 12, Abridge. 13, Epaulet. 14, Sum. 15, Racer. 17, Agnes. 18, Sweep. 20, Lower. 22, Map. 24, Eyeless. 25, Resists. 26, Two. 27, Collide. 28, Vitiate. 29, Rambler rose.

Down: 1, Programme seller. 2, Launder. 3, Scene. 4, Rotten Row. 5, Nirvana. 6, Spelling mistake. 7, Sprays. 8, Status. 16, Cold steel. 18, Speech. 19, Premium. 21, Risotto. 23, Poster. 25, Rover.

PUZZLE No. 36

Across: 1, Reached. 5, Praise. 9, Dukedom. 10, Embargo. 11, Cha. 12, Cable-stitch. 13, Lodge. 14, Furnished. 16, Sauntered. 17, Throb. 19, Interrupter. 22, Eel. 23, Armenia. 24, Prairie. 26, Freeze. 27, Remorse.

Down: 1, Radical. 2, Awkward customer. 3, Hod. 4, Demob. 5, Preferred. 6, Ambit. 7, Stretcher-bearer. 8, Coshed. 12, Chest. 14, Fortunate. 15, Inter. 16, Spiral. 18, Believe. 20, Range. 21, Toper. 25, Aim.

PUZZLE No. 37

Across: 1, Sherry-cobbler. 8, Mesh. 9, Lap. 10, Garish. 11, Pernicious. 13, Heir. 14, Angela. 16, Enduring. 19, Sinister. 22, Trench. 25, Arms. 26, Finisterre. 27, Gallon. 28, Cha. 29, Trot. 30, Surprise party.

Down: 1, Shebeen. 2, Enhance. 3, Reluctant. 4, Cup. 5, Bogus. 6, Lurcher. 7, Russian. 12, Overrun. 15, Gun. 17, Date stamp. 18, Ian. 20, Inroads. 21, Insular. 23, Erector. 24, Cursory. 26, Finer. 28, Cos.

PUZZLE No. 38

Across: 1, Prize-fighter. 8, Example. 9, Laid low. 11, Extraction. 12, Asti. 14, Cockatoo. 16, Tousle. 17, Nip. 19, Marble. 21, Last hope. 24, Dupe. 25, Incoherent. 27, Learner. 28, Average. 29, Tennis-racket.

Down: 1, Plastic. 2, Implacable. 3, Election. 4, Igloos. 5, Hail. 6, Enlists. 7, Defence Medal. 10, White heather. 13, Bottle-neck. 15, Oil. 18, Panorama. 20, Replace. 22, Overact. 23, Ingres. 26, Anon.

PUZZLE No. 39

Across: 6, Inverted commas. 9, Window. 10, Protract. 11, Shambles. 13, Assume. 15, Notice. 17, Denial. 19, Stroll. 20, Traverse. 22, Purchase. 24, Exhume. 26, Thieves' kitchen.

Down: 1, Finishing touch. 2, Avid. 3, Trowel. 4, Accolade. 5, Omar. 7, Expose. 8, Accomplishment. 12, Motto. 14, Slide. 16, Collated. 18, Streak. 21, Averts. 23, Chef. 25, Ha-ha.

PUZZLE No. 40

Across: 1, Terrific. 5, Market. 9, Decrease. 10, Honour. 12, Lord. 13, Rectangles. 15, Worldly wisdom. 19, Treasure trove. 23, Absolution. 25, Cape. 28, Grouse. 29, Sprinter. 30, Eleven. 31, Producer.

Down: 1, Toddle. 2, Recur. 3, Idea. 4, Instead. 6, Acorn. 7, Knowledge. 8, Tiresome. 11, Stay. 14, Iris. 15, Whetstone. 16, Lie. 17, Iron. 18, Strangle. 20, Rota. 21, Trooper. 22, Bearer. 24, Lisle. 26, Antic. 27, Wild.

PUZZLE No. 41

Across: 1, Let off steam. 9, Prairie. 10, Bayonet. 11, Ass. 12, Obelisk. 13, Thinner. 14, Ton. 15, Robin. 17, Moody. 18, Other. 20, Great. 22, Sad. 24, Polecat. 25, Parasol. 26, Eel. 27, Arrival. 28, Amazing. 29, Harvest moon.

Down: 1, Leave in the lurch. 2, Terrier. 3, Freak. 4, Substance. 5, Elysium. 6, Man in possession. 7, Sprout. 8, Stormy. 16, Bagatelle. 18, Orphan. 19, Recover. 21, Tornado. 23, Deluge. 25, Plant.

PUZZLE No. 42

Across: 1, Naphtha. 5, Punish. 9, Scruple. 10, Angular. 11, Bee. 12, Specialists. 13, Get-up. 14, Soundness. 16, Alternate. 17, Idiom. 19, Draw the line. 22, Tin. 23, Nagging. 24, Learner. 26, Crater. 27, Retreat.

Down: 1, Nosebag. 2, Perfect stranger. 3, Tip. 4, Adele. 5, Platitude. 6, Nigel. 7, Sales resistance. 8, Crisis. 12, Super. 14, Scavenger. 15, Drive. 16, Adding. 18, Minaret. 20, Twist. 21, Idler. 25, Art.

PUZZLE No. 43

Across: 1, Hit the jackpot. 8, Adam. 9, Gab. 10, Animal. 11, Patrolling. 13, Buff. 14, Beflag. 16, Presence. 19, Mandates. 22, Isabel. 25, Chef. 26, Providence. 27, Potato. 28, Pea. 29, Down. 30, Every other day.

Down: 1, Hydrate. 2, Tumbril (or-el). 3, Highlight. 4, Job. 5, Clang. 6, Pliable. 7, Traffic. 12, Impasto. 15, Fan. 17, Eliminate. 18, Nab. 20, Athlone. 21, Deflate. 23, Amended. 24, Each way. 26, Peony. 28, Pet.

PUZZLE No. 44

Across: 1, Dutch courage. 8, Radiant. 9, Tumbles. 11, Accusation. 12, Vera. 14, Hesitant. 16, Plunge. 17, Doh. 19, Lotion. 21, Research. 24, Slap. 25, Negotiator. 27, Rangoon. 28, Ingrate. 29, Order of Merit.

Down: 1, Deducts. 2, Transition. 3, Hatstand. 4, Option. 5, Rome. 6, Galleon. 7, Breathalyser. 10, Snake-charmer. 13, Glee-singer. 15, Tor. 18, Hedonism. 20, Trainer. 22, Retract. 23, Lean-to. 26, Cope.

PUZZLE No. 45

Across: 6, Leeward Islands. 9, Scampi. 10, Derelict. 11, Graceful. 13, Gothic. 15, Chance. 17, Alumni. 19, Tunnel. 20, Amperage. 22, Streamer. 24, Rubber. 26, Bring up the rear.

Down: 1, Electric guitar. 2, Team. 3, Tariff. 4, Astragal. 5, Wall. 7, Diddle. 8, Declining years. 12, Chain. 14, Tamar. 16, Columbus. 18, Parrot. 21, Porter. 23, Erne. 25, Beer.

PUZZLE No. 46

Across: 1, Slag-heap. 5, Stupid. 9, Surmount. 10, Antrim. 12, Eddy. 13, Stepmother. 15, Property owner. 19, Rag-and-bone man. 23, Practising. 25, Area. 28, Settle. 29, Stranger. 30, Laying. 31, Sporadic.

Down: 1, Sister. 2, Acrid. 3, Hoop. 4, Annette. 6, Tango. 7, Parthenon. 8, Demerara. 11, Spot. 14, Moon. 15, Pageantry. 16, Rio. 17, Ohms. 18, Proposal. 20, Bask. 21, Nonstop. 22, Fabric. 24, Talon. 26, Rigid. 27, Fair.

PUZZLE No. 47

Across: 1, Atmospheric. 9, Caterer. 10, Gallant. 11, Ash. 12, Limping. 13, Swinger. 14, Set. 15, Lucre. 17, Glory. 18, Wader. 20, Ledge. 22, See. 24, Lounges. 25, Present. 26, Pea. 27, Old-time. 28, Pungent. 29, Regular army.

Down: 1, Attempted murder. 2, Martial. 3, Scrag. 4, High-speed. 5, Rolling. 6, Change of scenery. 7, Sculls. 8, Stormy. 16, Cold spell. 18, Willow. 19, Rigging. 21, Eleanor. 23, Entity. 25, Paper.

PUZZLE No. 48

Across: 1, Cork tip. 5, Slight. 9, Railway. 10, Engrave. 11, Ass. 12, Expeditious. 13, Knoll. 14, Protector. 16, Dependant. 17, Great. 19, Indications. 22, One. 23, Talents. 24, Corners. 26, Byword. 27, Ribston.

Down: 1, Car park. 2, Rain stopped play. 3, Tow. 4, Pay up. 5, Speedboat. 6, Ingot. 7, Heat of the moment. 8, Censor. 12, Ellen. 14, Practised. 15, Edges. 16, Dainty. 18, Treason. 20, Canto. 21, Occur. 25, Rub.

PUZZLE No. 49

Across: 1, Fits and starts. 8, Lime. 9, Dig. 10, Robber. 11, Passionate. 13, Unit. 14, Seance. 16, Baby doll. 19, Debonair. 22, Carton. 25, Apse. 26, Franciscan. 27, Repair. 28, Ago. 29, Iron. 30, Sweet nothings.

Down: 1, Frigate. 2, Treason. 3, Andromeda. 4, Dog. 5, Three. 6, Rebound. 7, Special. 12, Alberta. 15, Alb. 17, Backcloth. 18, Out. 20, Express. 21, Operate. 23, Russian. 24, Orators. 26, First. 28, Ado.

PUZZLE No. 50

Across: 1, Supernatural. 8, Cuckold. 9, Unearth. 11, Originated. 12, Lion. 14, Lancelot. 16, Geneva. 17, RAF. 19, Aspect. 21, Battered. 24, Trek. 25, Prospector. 27, Railing. 28, Theatre. 29, Twelve months.

Down: 1, Section. 2, Prominence. 3, Radiator. 4, Amused. 5, Used. 6, Air line. 7, Schoolmaster. 10, Hans Andersen. 13, Settlement. 15, Tab. 18, Falsetto. 20, Preview. 22, Rotates. 23, Brogue. 26, Mill.

PUZZLE No. 51

Across: 6, Leaps and bounds. 9, Bridge. 10, Indirect. 11, Animated. 13, Expose. 15, Malady. 17, Strain. 19, Osiers. 20, Set aside. 22, Manitoba. 24, Iceman. 26, Become airborne.

Down: 1, Glaring mistake. 2, Band. 3, Assent. 4, Obedient. 5, Purr. 7, Naiads. 8, Ducks and drakes. 12, Melee. 14, Peals. 16, Discover. 18, Askari. 21, Trilby. 23, Idol. 25, Earl.

PUZZLE No. 52

Across: 1, Perforce. 5, Speech. 9, War paint. 10, Dispel. 12, Ella. 13, Collateral. 15, Intermediates. 19, Imperfections. 23, Delightful. 25, Dial. 28, Alison. 29, Pipeclay. 30, Skewer. 31, Streamer.

Down: 1, Powder. 2, Rural. 3, Opal. 4, Contour. 6, Point. 7, Euphrates. 8, Helpless. 11, Blue. 14, Star. 15, Impulsive. 16, Mac. 17, Iron. 18, Windlass. 20, Eats. 21, Tourist. 22, Player. 24, Goose. 26, Islam. 27, Hebe.

PUZZLE No. 53

Across: 1, Ace of Spades. 9, Leonine. 10, Oceania. 11, Elf. 12, Payment. 13, Endowed. 14, Ego. 15, Ticks. 17, Ducat. 18, Gusto. 20, Turns. 22, Ill. 24, Overall. 25, Camilla. 26, Owl. 27, Sitting. 28, Intense. 29, Runner-beans.

Down: 1, Anonymous letter. 2, Eminent. 3, Fleet. 4, Professor. 5, Dreaded. 6, Sandwich Islands. 7, Elapse. 8, Bandit. 16, Catalogue. 18, Grouse. 19, Ovation. 21, Sumatra. 23, Leader. 25, Climb.

PUZZLE No. 54

Across: 1, Deposit. 5, Quartz. 9, Sandbag. 10, Appease. 11, Ago. 12, Entitlement. 13, Facet. 14, Scrambled. 16, Genealogy. 17, Throb. 19, Opinion poll. 22, Tom. 23, Trigger. 24, Gambles. 26, Unwell. 27, Nemesis.

Down: 1, Distaff. 2, Pink of condition. 3, Sob. 4, Tight. 5, Quarterly. 6, Apple. 7, Travellers' tales. 8, Vested. 12, Extra. 14, Scoundrel. 15, Motel. 16, Growth. 18, Bemuses. 20, Ingle. 21, Organ. 25, Mum.

PUZZLE No. 55

Across: 1, Maid of all work. 8, Gaff. 9, Elm. 10, Inrush. 11, Refreshing. 13, Mark. 14, Strong. 16, Friendly. 19, Departed. 22, Dismay. 25, Opal. 26, Solicitude.

27, League. 28, Cat. 29, Lobe. 30, Shopping spree.
Down: 1, Meanest. 2, Inferno. 3, Oversight. 4, Aim. 5, Lying. 6, Oarsman. 7, Kestrel. 12, Infidel. 15, Rap. 17, Indicates. 18, Dam. 20, Express. 21, Allegro. 23, Settler. 24, Audible. 26, Steep. 28, Can.

PUZZLE No. 56

Across: 1, Incapacitate. 8, Incomer. 9, Islamic. 11, Canalising. 12, Moon. 14, Preacher. 16, Affair. 17, Dip. 19, Enmity. 21, Greeting. 24, Hand. 25, Consultant. 27, Portico. 28, Mansion. 29, Thick and thin.
Down: 1, Incense. 2, Complicate. 3, Perished. 4, Client. 5, Till. 6, Tombola. 7, Discipleship. 10, Congregating. 13, After lunch. 15, Rig. 18, Presumed. 20, Monarch. 22, Italian. 23, Corona. 26, Zinc.

PUZZLE No. 57

Across: 6, Push the boat out. 9, Breeze. 10, Serenade. 11, Stiletto. 13, Deport. 15, Notion. 17, Broken. 19, Stance. 20, Tamarisk. 22, Obstacle. 24, Roughs. 26, Pearls of wisdom.
Down: 1, Operating table. 2, Isle. 3, Street. 4, Corridor. 5, Stun. 7, Euston. 8, Under one's thumb. 12, Latin. 14, Poker. 16, Overcast. 18, Itself. 21, Martin. 23, Tory. 25, Undo.

PUZZLE No. 58

Across: 1, Fearsome. 5, Octavo. 9, Syndrome. 10, Muscle. 12, East. 13, Interposed. 15, See how they run. 19, Consequential. 23, Accrington. 25, Coma. 28, Picket. 29, Pleasant. 30, Dwells. 31, Asterisk.
Down: 1, Fasten. 2, Agnes. 3, Serf. 4, Memento. 6, Chump. 7, Ancestral. 8, Overdone. 11, Bent. 14, Here. 15, Song-cycle. 16, Woe. 17, Evil. 18, Scrapped. 20, Urge. 21, Noodles. 22, Bartok. 24, Ideal. 26, Okapi. 27, Cape.

PUZZLE No. 59

Across: 1, Sailor's knot. 9, Elevate. 10, Angular. 11, Sit. 12, Coppice. 13, Enliven. 14, Nun. 15, Noble. 17, Dusty. 18, Cadiz. 20, Outer. 22, Old. 24, Scabies. 25, Debated. 26, Hue. 27, Luggage. 28, Parable. 29, Two of a trade.
Down: 1, Sleeping-draught. 2, Italian. 3, Obese. 4, Statement. 5, Niggled. 6, Television table. 7, Beacon. 8, Frenzy. 16, Bookshelf. 18, Castle. 19, Zhivago. 21, Roberta. 23, Dodger. 25, Depot.

PUZZLE No. 60

Across: 1, Radiant. 5, Praise. 9, Pigment. 10, Princes. 11, Ski. 12, Consequence. 13, Egham. 14, Improvise. 16, Newmarket. 17, Niche. 19, Deteriorate. 22, Mat. 23, Skillet. 24, Embrace. 26, Ashore. 27, Abridge.
Down: 1, Riposte. 2, Dog with two tails. 3, Ape. 4, Titan. 5, Pepperpot. 6, Adieu. 7, Second in command. 8, Essene. 12, Comma. 14, Ink-bottle. 15, Ounce. 16, Nudist. 18, Extreme. 20, Rollo. 21, Arena. 25, Bar.

PUZZLE No. 61

Across: 1, Maids of honour. 8, Iris. 9, Asp. 10, Steppe. 11, Inventions. 13, Nous. 14, Crater. 16, Endpaper. 19, Stranded. 22, Shandy. 25, Tyro. 26, Clever Dick. 27, Shrove. 28, Eli. 29, Elmo. 30, Polite refusal.
Down: 1, Mariner. 2, Inspect. 3, Shattered. 4, Fop. 5, Oasis. 6, Oceania. 7, Rapture. 12, Overdue. 15, Air. 17, Disbelief. 18, Pen. 20, Toyshop. 21, Axolotl. 23, Address. 24, Decimal. 26, Chest. 28, Ear.

PUZZLE No. 62

Across: 1, Incarcerated. 8, Ravines. 9, Pooh-bah. 11, Motherwell. 12, Drag. 14, Sideshow. 16, Got off. 17, Dad. 19, Edison. 21, Repulsed. 24, Mail. 25, Immaterial. 27, Rais-

ing. 28, Extract. 29, Glowing terms.
Down: 1, Invited. 2, Conversion. 3, Rosewood. 4, Expels. 5, Avon. 6, Embargo. 7, Tramp steamer. 10, High fidelity. 13, Lotus-eater. 15, War. 18, Decadent. 20, Initial. 22, Spirals. 23, Imogen. 26, View.

PUZZLE No. 63

Across: 6, On with the dance. 9, Edible. 10, Watchers. 11, Brighton. 13, Output. 15, Astray. 17, Stigma. 19, Sample. 20, Tell-tale. 22, Disposal. 24, Thirty. 26, Pensionable age.
Down: 1, Powder magazine. 2, Swab. 3, Attest. 4, Beetroot. 5, Wash. 7, Towing. 8, Circular letter. 12, Get-up. 14, Tight. 16, Aversion. 18, Stella. 21, Little. 23, Push. 25, Iran.

PUZZLE No. 64

Across: 1, Buffalo Bill. 9, Curtain. 10, Shingle. 11, Ire. 12, Episode. 13, Roasted. 14, Mug. 15, Sepia. 17, Exile. 18, Pluto. 20, Rated. 22, Gas. 24, Lesotho. 25, Sparkle. 26, Nut. 27, Opinion. 28, Elector. 29, Needle match.
Down: 1, Burning question. 2, Flagons. 3, Annie. 4, Observant. 5, Imitate. 6, Lightning sketch. 7, Scream. 8, Meddle. 16, Personnel. 18, Pallor. 19, Outline. 21, Dialect. 23, Sherry. 25, Steam.

PUZZLE No. 65

Across: 1, Skipper. 5, Accost. 9, Rattled. 10, Verbose. 11, Tie. 12, Cirencester. 13, Human. 14, Soundings. 16, Colleague. 17, Eight. 19, Exhibitions. 22, Lie. 23, Elusive. 24, Segment. 26, Usurer. 27, Samoyed.
Down: 1, Scratch. 2, In the small hours. 3, Pal. 4, Radar. 5, Adventure. 6, Curve. 7, Shooting gallery. 8, Hearts. 12, Canoe. 14, Sightseer. 15, Dress. 16, Clever. 18, Treated. 20, Briar (or-er). 21, Oasis. 25, Gum.

PUZZLE No. 66

Across: 1, Willow pattern. 8, Pomp. 9, Elm. 10, Thelma. 11, Reversible. 13, Also. 14, Lapdog. 16, Nameless. 19, Operetta. 22, Repent. 25, Tess. 26, Spellbound. 27, Pillar. 28, Ass. 29, Open. 30, Murder mystery.
Down: 1, Woomera. 2, Lip-read. 3, Oversight. 4, Pam. 5, Title. 6, Eyeball. 7, Nemesis. 12, Bandage. 15, Pie. 17, Moralises. 18, Ewe. 20, Premium. 21, Rustler. 23, Provoke. 24, Nunnery. 26, Spree. 28, Aim.

PUZZLE No. 67

Across: 1, Commissioner. 8, Onestep. 9, Pointer. 11, Astronomer. 12, Disc. 14, Strolled. 16, Unreal. 17, Red. 19, Potash. 21, Wiseacre. 24, Orbs. 25, Discordant. 27, Ticking. 28, Ontario. 29, Comprehended.
Down: 1, Chester. 2, Motionless. 3, Improver. 4, Supper. 5, Odin. 6, Entwine. 7, Moral support. 10, Recollection. 13, Underrated. 15, Dew. 18, Disclose. 20, Tobacco. 22, Chaired. 23, Single. 26, Limp.

PUZZLE No. 68

Across: 6, House detective. 9, Ushant. 10, Cheapest. 11, Bootless. 13, Ticket. 15, Accept. 17, Alkali. 19, Chisel. 20, Obdurate. 22, Enclosed. 24, Mature. 26, Behind the times.
Down: 1, Ghost of a chance. 2, Aura. 3, Beetle. 4, Pedestal. 5, Stop. 7, Excise. 8, Vested interest. 12, Tacks. 14, Chair. 16, Palisade. 18, Howdah. 21, Dimity. 23, Lair. 25, Tame.

PUZZLE No. 69

Across: 1, Goalpost. 5, Buffer. 9, Undulate. 10, Sports. 12, Gasp. 13, Rhetorical. 15, Battle honours. 19, Endurance test. 23, Hair-spring. 25, Step. 28, Ration. 29, Abdicate. 30, Ernest. 31, Seasonal.
Down: 1, Grudge. 2, Andes. 3, Pill.

4, Satchel. 6, Upper. 7, Forecourt. 8, Restless. 11, Itch. 14, Stir. 15, Badminton. 16, Etc. 17, Need. 18, Sea-horse. 20, Nark. 21, Ennoble. 22, Appeal. 24, Shoes. 26, Train. 27, Bias.

PUZZLE No. 70

Across: 1, Bathing pool. 9, Crusade. 10, Tactile. 11, Age. 12, Rotates. 13, Smasher. 14, Bun. 15, Rifle. 17, Drone. 18, Hitch. 20, Rides. 22, Bob. 24, Neutron. 25, Freezer. 26, Ill. 27, Seeking. 28, Appease. 29, Take the lead.

Down: 1, Blunt instrument. 2, Traitor. 3, Ideas. 4, Gateshead. 5, Orchard. 6, Leighton Buzzard. 7, Scarab. 8, Degree. 16, Fortnight. 18, Honest. 19, Herrick. 21, Steeple. 23, Barter. 25, Flame.

PUZZLE No. 71

Across: 1, Diarist. 5, Rattle. 9, Strange. 10, Preface. 11, Air. 12, Battledress. 13, Fifty. 14, Whitehall. 16, Incursive. 17, Tudor. 19, Perfect Lady. 22, Ida. 23, Chicago. 24, Bagshot. 26, Priest. 27, Exposed.

Down: 1, Distaff. 2, Aircraft carrier. 3, Inn. 4, Trent. 5, Repulsive. 6, Tread. 7, Loaves and fishes. 8, Weasel. 12, Boyar. 14, Waistcoat. 15, Entry. 16, Impact. 18, Reacted. 20, Evade. 21, Amble. 25, Gap.

PUZZLE No. 72

Across: 1, Ruling passion. 8, Bang. 9, Van. 10, Grouse. 11, Distillery. 13, Idea. 14, Debris. 16, Arrogate. 19, Proposal. 22, Grants. 25, Plan. 26, Side-stroke. 27, Divine. 28, Toe. 29, Aunt. 30, Smelling-salts.

Down: 1, Realise (or -ze). 2, Lighter. 3, Novelists. 4, Pin. 5, Soggy. 6, Ironing. 7, Nascent. 12, Enabled. 15, Boo. 17, Registers. 18, Ann. 20, Rallies. 21, Pensive. 23, Air mail. 24, Takings. 26, Shell. 28, Tin.

PUZZLE No. 73

Across: 1, Pepper's ghost. 8, Shaving. 9, Onestep. 11, Articulate. 12, Cake. 14, Occupier. 16, Inhere. 17, Doh. 19, Outset. 21, Daylight. 24, Iron. 25, Contestant. 27, Tug-boat. 28, Orinoco. 29, Stage-manager.

Down: 1, Plastic. 2, Principles. 3, Engulfed. 4, Shorts. 5, Heed. 6, Satiate. 7, Escapologist. 10, Presentation. 13, Unclasping. 15, Rod. 18, Hawthorn. 20, Thought. 22, Glamour. 23, Bottom. 26, Song.

PUZZLE No. 74

Across: 6, On the off-chance. 9, Pebble. 10, Toddling. 11, Immortal. 13, Meagre. 15, Oliver. 17, Scrawl. 19, Cheese. 20, November. 22, Starfish. 24, Curate. 26, Blow the man down.

Down: 1, Honeymoon hotel. 2, Stub. 3, Behest. 4, Academic. 5, Wall. 7, Fettle. 8, Central heating. 12, Opine. 14, Alarm. 16, Eyesight. 18, Anthem. 21, Vacant. 23, Rows. 25, Rook.

PUZZLE No. 75

Across: 1, Air-frame. 5, Ostler. 9, Monotony. 10, Morsel. 12, Doom. 13, Disruptive. 15, Beyond measure. 19, Lady of leisure. 23, Cogitation. 25, Harp. 28, Coarse. 29, Mitigate. 30, Tidier. 31, Bedstead.

Down: 1, Armada. 2, Rondo. 3, Rite. 4, Mansion. 6, Scoop. 7, Lassitude. 8, Relieved. 11, Drum. 14, Tyro. 15, Bodyguard. 16, Due. 17, Arum. 18, Black cat. 20, Lute. 21, Idolise. 22, Spread. 24, Taste. 26, Aware. 27, Miss.

PUZZLE No. 76

Across: 1, Battle royal. 9, Robbing. 10, Freight. 11, Err. 12, Dilates. 13, Auditor. 14, Era. 15, Elfin. 17, Dried. 18, Radio. 20, Andes. 22, Gap. 24, Bequest. 25, Berates. 26, Use. 27, Shearer. 28, Section. 29, Kingdom-come.

Down: 1, Bubble-and-squeak. 2,

Thistle. 3, Loges. 4, Refrained. 5, Yielded. 6, Lightning strike. 7, Bridge. 8, Stored. 16, Fractured. 18, Robust. 19, Overrun. 21, Sirocco. 23, Posing. 25, Besom.

PUZZLE No. 77

Across: 1, Reposed. 5, Salary. 9, Loretta. 10, Instant. 11, Pro. 12, Grandmother. 13, Erase. 14, Guildford. 16, Broadcast. 17, Inter. 19, Luggage-rack. 22, Egg. 23, Evasive. 24, Sea-room. 26, Haunts. 27, Shannon.

Down: 1, Relapse. 2, Persona non grata. 3, Set. 4, Drama. 5, Spindrift. 6, Lasso. 7, Reach for the moon. 8, Stared. 12, Greed. 14, Graceless. 15, Drink. 16, Ballet. 18, Regimen. 20, Alien. 21, Asses. 25, Aga.

PUZZLE No. 78

Across: 1, Salad dressing. 8, Form. 9, Sap. 10, Beaten. 11, Face-powder. 13, Ivan. 14, Settle. 16, Absentee. 19, Surveyor. 22, Amanda. 25, Scar. 26, Remarkable. 27, Result. 28, Pea. 29, Side. 30, Rule of the road.

Down: 1, Storage. 2, Lambent. 3, Discovery. 4, Rip. 5, Sober. 6, Italian. 7, Grenade. 12, Diagram. 15, Tar. 17, Staircase. 18, Ton. 20, Unclear. 21, Virtual. 23, Alassio. 24, Deluded. 26, Ratio. 28, Pot.

PUZZLE No. 79

Across: 1, Respectfully. 8, Numbers. 9, Palette. 11, Undertaker. 12, Grip. 14, Bulletin. 16, Angler. 17, Cur. 19, Arcade. 21, Telegram. 24, Cone. 25, Contention. 27, Sea-lion. 28, Brescia. 29, Carpet-beater.

Down: 1, Remodel. 2, Spearheads. 3, Ecstatic. 4, Tippet. 5, Ugly. 6, Lateral. 7, Encumbrances. 10, Experimental. 13, Internment. 15, Nut. 18, Rentable. 20, Cantata. 22, Rail-car. 23, Hornet. 26, Limp.

PUZZLE No. 80

Across: 6, One of the family. 9, Middle. 10, Applauds. 11, Ascended. 13, Induce. 15, Norman.

17, Stigma. 19, Crater. 20, Cogitate. 22, Aspirant. 24, Misery. 26, Medicine bottle.

Down: 1, Robinson Crusoe. 2, Lead. 3, Offend. 4, Offprint. 5, Emma. 7, Hoards. 8, Lady Chatterley. 12, Egret. 14, Digit. 16, Adriatic. 18, Scythe. 21, Gambol. 23, Isis. 25, Site.

PUZZLE No. 81

Across: 1, Calamity. 5, Ambled. 9, Cupboard. 10, Probes. 12, Link. 13, Purchasing. 15, Rough estimate. 19, Model aircraft. 23, Renovation. 25, Able. 28, Cradle. 29, Opposite. 30, Nether. 31, Fragment.

Down: 1, Cackle. 2, Lupin. 3, Mood. 4, Through. 6, Maria. 7, Lubricant. 8, Designer. 11, Acts. 14, Hull. 15, Redundant. 16, Ear. 17, Iran. 18, American. 20, Iota. 21, Chopper. 22, Cement. 24, Value. 26, Bride. 27, Long.

PUZZLE No. 82

Across: 1, Shock-troops. 9, Scruple. 10, Aniline. 11, Ass. 12, Awkward. 13, Stammer. 14, Eon. 15, Sober. 17, Inner. 18, Basis. 20, Indus. 22, Cap. 24, Nacelle. 25, Refusal. 26, Woe. 27, Average. 28, Torture. 29, Small change.

Down: 1, Striking success. 2, Orphans. 3, Knead. 4, Reassured. 5, Origami. 6, Swimming costume. 7, Estate. 8, Bearer. 16, Bridewell. 18, Banyan. 19, Sultana. 21, Saffron. 23, Pallet. 25, Retch.

PUZZLE No. 83

Across: 1, Bubbles. 5, Scrape. 9, Regatta. 10, Bran-tub. 11, Tan. 12, Regulations. 13, Anent. 14, Pressures. 16, Obsession. 17, Inter. 19, Tale-bearing. 22, Odd. 23, Example. 24, Stamina. 26, Tender. 27, Tonight.

Down: 1, Biretta. 2, Beginners please. 3, Lot. 4, Slang. 5, Subaltern. 6, Roast. 7, Petrol rationing.

8, Abuses. 12, Rites. 14, Privateer. 15, Swing. 16, Outlet. 18, Radiant. 20, Biped. 21, Inset. 25, Ann.

PUZZLE No. 84

Across: 1, Debt collector. 8, Oral. 9, Ebb. 10, Garage. 11, Difference. 13, Able. 14, Tralee. 16, Whitelaw. 19, Carlisle. 22, Stress. 25, Area. 26, Freeloader. 27, Inside. 28, Pin. 29, Ibis. 30, Eightsome reel.

Down: 1, Dirtier. 2, Baleful. 3, Cheerless. 4, Lob. 5, Eagle. 6, Terrace. 7, Regalia. 12, Nowhere. 15, Air. 17, Insolence. 18, Lee. 20, Arrange. 21, Leaping. 23, Realise. 24, Special. 26, Fleet. 28, Pro.

PUZZLE No. 85

Across: 1, Commissioner. 8, Romance. 9, Chevron. 11, Toleration. 12, Blow. 14, Sextants. 16, Scipio. 17, Yes. 19, Mascot. 21, Waterman. 24, Road. 25, Collateral. 27, Heiress. 28, Ovation. 29, Here and there.

Down: 1, Complex. 2, Minor canon. 3, Identity. 4, Sector. 5, Open. 6, Ear-flap. 7, Protest march. 10, Newfoundland. 13, Accentuate. 15, Sew. 18, Sail-loft. 20, Seaside. 22, Martine. 23, Hobson. 26, Bede.

PUZZLE No. 86

Across: 6, Halfpenny stamp. 9, Enable. 10, Epigraph. 11, Reversal. 13, Distil. 15, Salute. 17, Priest. 19, Signal. 20, Hosepipe. 22, Emphatic. 24, Outset. 26, Trouble in store.

Down: 1, Channel swimmer. 2, Club. 3, Uppers. 4, Cylinder. 5, Star. 7, Needle. 8, Mephistopheles. 12, Ellen. 14, Steep. 16, Tell-tale. 18, Chichi. 21, Spouse. 23, Hour. 25, Troy.

PUZZLE No. 87

Across: 1, Dipstick. 5, Abacus. 9, Internal. 10, Nutmeg. 12, Earl. 13, Ingredient. 15, Double portion. 19, Unfashionable. 23, Reinstated. 25, Inca. 28, Equals. 29, Alhambra. 30, Settee. 31, Psaltery.

Down: 1, Driver. 2, Peter. 3, Term. 4, Channel. 6, Bound. 7, Cymbeline. 8, Sighting. 11, Trip. 14, Puss. 15, Difficult. 16, Ego. 17, Ruby. 18, Quarters. 20, Iran. 21, Needles. 22, Canary. 24, Solve. 26, Noble. 27, Wall.

PUZZLE No. 88

Across: 1, Ugly Sisters. 9, Radical. 10, Radiant. 11, Via. 12, Marquee. 13, Marlene. 14, Yah. 15, Easel. 17, Edict. 18, Towns. 20, Verge. 22, Egg. 24, Roadman. 25, Chester. 26, Too. 27, Unhinge. 28, Motions. 29, Ruling class.

Down: 1, Under the weather. 2, Lecture. 3, Salve. 4, Scrambler. 5, Endorse. 6, Stage directions. 7, Grumpy. 8, Street. 16, Seventeen. 18, Torque. 19, Seminal. 21, Electra. 23, Garish. 25, Comic.

PUZZLE No. 89

Across: 1, Balloon. 5, Sesame. 9, Talents. 10, Thought. 11, Two. 12, Distraction. 13, Baton. 14, Destroyed. 16, Overrates. 17, Caned. 19, Fragmentary. 22, Gas. 23, Cellist. 24, Tillage. 26, Oyster. 27, Creased.

Down: 1, Bathtub. 2, Lily of the valley. 3, Own. 4, Noses. 5, Satirists. 6, Stoic. 7, Magnifying glass. 8, Stoned. 12, Donor. 14, Detonator. 15, Rocky. 16, Office. 18, Distend. 20, Moist. 21, Attic. 25, Lee.

PUZZLE No. 90

Across: 1, Police-station. 8, Bang. 9, Eat. 10, Steppe. 11, Recompense. 13, Arum. 14, Dorset. 16, Grandees. 19, Estimate. 22, Ticket. 25, Saga. 26, Determined. 27, Flying. 28, Spa. 29, Kith. 30, Window-cleaner.

Down: 1, Placebo. 2, Legions. 3, Cleopatra. 4, Set. 5, Aisle. 6, Iceland. 7, Neptune. 12, Neglect. 15,

Rut. 17, Alternate. 18, Elk. 20, Swallow. 21, Italian. 23, Chicken. 24, Elector. 26, Doggo. 28, Sec.

PUZZLE No. 91

Across: 1, Security risk. 8, Whirred. 9, Cowslip. 11, Extenuated. 12, Knee. 14, Worthing. 16, Covers. 17, Ted. 19, Legman. 21, Northern. 24, Iona. 25, Typewriter. 27, Maestro. 28, Thistle. 29, Playing-cards.
Down: 1, Snifter. 2, Corinthian. 3, Red paint. 4, Tacked. 5, Rows. 6, Silence. 7, Sweet-william. 10, Pleasantries. 13, Fox-terrier. 15, Gen. 18, Domestic. 20, Genteel. 22, Estates. 23, Tycoon. 26, Stay.

PUZZLE No. 92

Across: 6, Abraham Lincoln. 9, Inches. 10, Luminary. 11, Symbolic. 13, Tattoo. 15, Higher. 17, Bright. 19, Crisis. 20, Importer. 22, Advocate. 24, Coffin. 26, Pyramid selling.
Down: 1, Maundy Thursday. 2, Arch. 3, Chisel. 4, Diameter. 5, Icon. 7, Malice. 8, Lord of the Rings. 12, Bogus. 14, Tiger. 16, Ecstatic. 18, Divers. 21, Pickle. 23, Oman. 25, Flip.

PUZZLE No. 93

Across: 1, Post code. 5, Abacus. 9, Congress. 10, Gambol. 12, Eden. 13, Management. 15, Man of the world. 19, Words of wisdom. 23, Triangular. 25, Abut. 28, Hailed. 29, Victoria. 30, Sudden. 31, Heighten.
Down: 1, Packet. 2, Sense. 3, Corn. 4, Distaff. 6, Brake. 7, Cablegram. 8, Solitude. 11, Wash. 14, Onus. 15, Mortified. 16, Tow. 17, Wade. 18, Switches. 20, Four. 21, Imagine. 22, Strain. 24, Niece. 26, Burst. 27, Stag.

PUZZLE No. 94

Across: 1, Parlour-maid. 9, Scruple. 10, Stature. 11, Rap. 12, Look-out. 13, Brawler. 14, Sum. 15, Facer.

17, Towel. 18, Mince. 20, Layer. 22, Ink. 24, Diffuse. 25, Fastens. 26, Col. 27, Elegant. 28, Outline. 29, Slender hope.
Down: 1, Performing fleas. 2, Reproof. 3, Overt. 4, Raspberry. 5, Adamant. 6, Double white line. 7, Psalms. 8, Petrol. 16, Collected. 18, Madder. 19, Emulate. 21, Risotto. 23, Kissed. 25, Floor.

PUZZLE No. 95

Across: 1, Panther. 5, Medici. 9, Novelty. 10, Trainee. 11, Awl. 12, Concealment. 13, Lenin. 14, Newcastle. 16, Starlight. 17, Rides. 19, Presentable. 22, Cha. 23, Electra. 24, Bearing. 26, Stance. 27, Learner.
Down: 1, Pinball. 2, Naval engagement. 3, Hal. 4, Rayon. 5, Motherwit. 6, Drawl. 7, Concerted action. 8, Beetle. 12, Canal. 14, Nightmare. 15, Agree. 16, Sapper. 18, Stagger. 20, Eaten. 21, Babel. 25, Ada.

PUZZLE No. 96

Across: 1, Doctor's orders. 8, Asti. 9, Tap. 10, Gaelic. 11, Racecourse. 13, Aide. 14, Geneva. 16, Bewilder. 19, Polisher. 22, Ogress. 25, Hero. 26, Leadership. 27, Radium. 28, Eel. 29, Lift. 30, Light-fingered.
Down: 1, Disease. 2, Chinese. 3, Osteopath. 4, Sop. 5, Rogue. 6, Eyeball. 7, Spindle. 12, Roberta. 15, Nil. 17, Wooden leg. 18, Due. 20, Overall. 21, Ironing. 23, Rustler. 24, Sniffed. 26, Limit. 28, Eli.

PUZZLE No. 97

Across: 1, Championship. 8, Drapery. 9, Fly-trap. 11, Astrologer. 12, Magi. 14, Concerto. 16, Kisses. 17, Ham. 19, Golden. 21, Football. 24, Alto. 25, Regimental. 27, Daubing. 28, Abstain. 29, Red-letter day.
Down: 1, Chasten. 2, Anemometer. 3, Plymouth. 4, Offset. 5, Skye. 6, Inroads. 7, Advance guard. 10,

Plimsoll line. 13, Distressed. 15, Oaf. 18, **Motivate**. 20, Lettuce. 22, Actuary. 23, **Weight**. 26, Fill.

PUZZLE No. 98

Across: 6, Half a sovereign. 9, Priest. 10, Notation. 11, Tea-chest. 13, Expect. 15, Hearts. 17, Esteem. 19, Persia. 20, Armenian. 22, Proposal. 24, Nereid. 26, Charlie Chaplin.

Down: 1, Charge the earth. 2, Glue. 3, Rattle. 4, Feathers. 5, Best. 7, Ornate. 8, Good Companions. 12, Class. 14, Preen. 16, Transmit. 18, Gallic. 21, Monday. 23, Port. 25, Role.

PUZZLE No. 99

Across: 1, Gatepost. 5, Moscow. 9, Seascape. 10, Vernon. 12, Ivan. 13, Second-rate. 15, House of Orange. 19, Vacuum-cleaner. 23, Ring-finger. 25, Stud. 28, Rhymer. 29, Manicure. 30, Widths. 31, Adorable.

Down: 1, Gossip. 2, Tiara. 3, Pack. 4, Supreme. 6, Oread. 7, Container. 8, Wanderer. 11, Loaf. 14, Lulu. 15, Hackneyed. 16, Oil. 17, Rank. 18, Overdraw. 20, Cane. 21, Emerald. 22, Adhere. 24, Flesh. 26, Thumb. 27, Liar.

PUZZLE No. 100

Across: 1, King William. 9, Evicted. 10, Panache. 11, Ear. 12, Scholar. 13, Epitaph. 14, Two. 15, Speed. 17, Nylon. 18, Motet. 20, Lyric. 22, Add. 24, Teeming. 25, Shudder. 26, Hot. 27, Realist. 28, Untried. 29, Helen of Troy.

Down: 1, Knight of the Bath. 2, Nettles. 3, Wider. 4, Lip-reader. 5, Inn-sign. 6, Michaelmas daisy. 7, Tea-set. 8, Peahen. 16, Enlighten. 18, Mature. 19, Trivial. 21, Counter. 23, Deride. 25, Stuff.

PUZZLE No. 101

Across: 1, Packing. 5, Stumps. 9, Elevate. 10, Cuticle. 11, Ink. 12, Temperature. 13, Wafer. 14, Shapeless. 16, Schoolboy. 17, Group. 19, Low comedian. 22, Tat. 23, Sorting. 24, Pottage. 26, Ascend. 27, Tuesday.

Down: 1, Preview. 2, Clerk of the works. 3, Ida. 4, Gleam. 5, Secretary. 6, Ultra. 7, Picture postcard. 8, Recess. 12, Torso. 14, Submerged. 15, Elgin. 16, Splash. 18, Pottery. 20, Opine. 21, Input. 25, Tie.

PUZZLE No. 102

Across: 1, Pure and simple. 8, Asti. 9, Sob. 10, Larder. 11, Immigrants. 13, Note. 14, Untrue. 16, Clipping. 19, Immortal. 22, Threat. 25, Free. 26, Saturnalia. 27, Shrine. 28, Bee. 29, Hate. 30, Regular reader.

Down: 1, Postman. 2, Rainier. 3, Absorbent. 4, Dab. 5, Isles. 6, Parsnip. 7, Everton. 12, Necklet. 15, Tom. 17, Interfere. 18, Ike. 20, Marcher. 21, Opening. 23, Reached. 24, Aviator. 26, Spell. 28, Bar.

PUZZLE No. 103

Across: 1, Asseveration. 8, Reading. 9, Chariot. 11, Distillery. 12, Pike. 14, Side-line. 16, Signet. 17, Tea. 19, Income. 21, Linchpin. 24, Acid. 25, Restaurant. 27, Eyeball. 28, Glamour. 29, Yellow streak.

Down: 1, Amassed. 2, Spirit-lamp. 3, Vigilant. 4, Record. 5, Teak. 6, Opinion. 7, Predestinate. 10, Treat in store. 13, Discourage. 15, Eel. 18, Airtight. 20, Chinese. 22, Peacock. 23, Fellow. 26, Wail.

PUZZLE No. 104

Across: 6, Line of approach. 9, Knight. 10, Clansman. 11, Accounts. 13, Easing. 15, Resume. 17, Stroll. 19, Prison. 20, Optimist. 22, Adherent. 24, Barman. 26, Never-never land.

Down: 1, Blank cartridge. 2, Snug. 3, Boston. 4, Apparent. 5, Moss. 7, Accost. 8, Channel Islands. 12, Oasis. 14, Storm. 16, Mantegna.

18, Rostov. 21, Tabard. 23, Even. 25, Real.

PUZZLE No. 105

Across: 1, Hornpipe. 5, Dancer. 9, Sabotage. 10, Glinka. 12, Lino. 13, Grotesques. 15, Plain-speaking. 19, Launching site. 23, Groundling. 25, Shoe. 28, Onrush. 29, Fruit-bat. 30, Extras. 31, Blighter.

Down: 1, Hustle. 2, Robin. 3, Pity. 4, Pig-iron. 6, Atlas. 7, Concubine. 8, Road sign. 11, Step. 14, Talc. 15, Plutocrat. 16, Sun. 17, Amin. 18, Flag-pole. 20, Isle. 21, General. 22, Rector. 24, Nesta. 26, Habit. 27, Wing.

PUZZLE No. 106

Across: 1, Maria Callas. 9, Runcorn. 10, Remorse. 11, Ike. 12, Maypole. 13, Endowed. 14, Ego. 15, Snake. 17, Grime. 18, Broom. 20, Antic. 22, Tod. 24, Cadence. 25, Showers. 26, Met. 27, Profane. 28, Opening. 29, Elastic band.

Down: 1, Money for old rope. 2, Riotous. 3, Annie. 4, Agreement. 5, Lame dog. 6, Straws in the wind. 7, Gramme. 8, Peddle. 16, Abasement. 18, Biceps. 19, Montana. 21, Cholera. 23, Design. 25, Stoic.

PUZZLE No. 107

Across: 1, Tablets. 5, Pariah. 9, Bowline. 10, Orbital. 11, Tor. 12, Meadow-sweet. 13, Aloft. 14, Concourse. 16, Metronome. 17, Topic. 19, Green fields. 22, Fan. 23, Tourist. 24, Banshee. 26, Player. 27, Lighted.

Down: 1, Tabitha. 2, Beware of the bull. 3, Eli. 4, Sheba. 5, Pronounce. 6, Robes. 7, At the drop of a hat. 8, Blithe. 12, Motto. 14, Chorister. 15, Oaths. 16, Mighty. 18, Contend. 20, Noisy. 21, Label. 25, Nag.

PUZZLE No. 108

Across: 1, Pebble glasses. 8, Boss. 9, Nip. 10, Glance. 11, Monopolist. 13, Feed. 14, Vernon. 16, Suspense. 19, Commerce. 22, Earned. 25, Stir. 26, Bedraggled. 27, Colour. 28, Odd. 29, Late. 30, Reign of terror.

Down: 1, Promote. 2, Bassoon. 3, Landowner. 4, Gap. 5, Aught. 6, Snaffle. 7, Success. 12, Instead. 15, Rum. 17, Skedaddle. 18, Nun. 20, Outsoar. 21, Marconi. 23, Regular. 24, Elector. 26, Baron. 28, Oaf.

PUZZLE No. 109

Across: 1, Cash and carry. 8, Handles. 9, Seizure. 11, Railwayman. 12, Mice. 14, Homeland. 16, Frieze. 17, God. 19, Archer. 21, Heaviest. 24, Dash. 25, Outlandish. 27, Nearest. 28, Rondeau. 29, Reassessment.

Down: 1, Confirm. 2, Self-willed. 3, Assaying. 4, Dismay. 5, Aria. 6, Routine. 7, Churchwarden. 10, Eleventh hour. 13, Provenance. 15, Doh. 18, Declares. 20, Cascade. 22, Evident. 23, Subtle. 26, Tees.

PUZZLE No. 110

Across: 6, Turn of the screw. 9, Odious. 10, Severity. 11, Converse. 13, Regent. 15, Unload. 17, Repeat. 19, Filter. 20, Mutation. 22, Internal. 24, Reduce. 26, Neanderthal man.

Down: 1, Studio audience. 2, Brio. 3, Mouser. 4, Peverse. 5, Scar. 7, Tester. 8, Extinct volcano. 12, Valet. 14, Great. 16, Arranged. 18, Amulet. 21, Torbay. 23, Erne. 25, Dome.

PUZZLE No. 111

Across: 1, Parasite. 5, Adopts. 9, Postcard. 10, Banner. 12, Also. 13, Visitation. 15, Credit squeeze. 19, Domestic bliss. 23, Iron maiden. 25, Coma. 28, Emigre. 29, Skinhead. 30, Saying. 31, Braggart.

Down: 1, Poplar. 2, Roses. 3, Sack. 4, Termini. 6, Drama. 7, Penniless. 8, Stranger. 11, Miss. 14, Tess. 15, Commodity. 16, Tic. 17, Unit. 18, Admirers. 20, Iris. 21, Breaker. 22,

Bandit. 24, Moron. 26, Opera. 27, Snug.

PUZZLE No. 112

Across: 1, Pillow-fight. 9, Arrange. 10, Ailment. 11, Rug. 12, Escheat. 13, Roaster. 14, You. 15, Satin. 17, Toque. 18, Trent. 20, Dream. 22, Elm. 24, Largely. 25, Scratch. 26, Boa. 27, Promote. 28, Tripoli. 29, Show results.

Down: 1, Parachute troops. 2, Lingers. 3, Overt. 4, Fragrance. 5, Gallant. 6, Twenty Questions. 7, Napery. 8, Starve. 16, Teddy-bear. 18, Tulips. 19, Tremolo. 21, Martial. 23, Mohair. 25, Sates.

PUZZLE No. 113

Across: 1, Chapter. 5, Arrive. 9, Reigned. 10, Immerse. 11, Age. 12, Provocation. 13, Hotel. 14, Trickster. 16, Mortality. 17, Earth. 19, Uncertified. 22, Inn. 23, Handful. 24, Flavour. 26, Clergy. 27, Relayed.

Down: 1, Car wash. 2, Alimentary canal. 3, Tan. 4, Radio. 5, Animosity. 6, Rumba. 7, Virgin territory. 8, Tenner. 12, Palma. 14, Trivially. 15, Knead. 16, Mouths. 18, Hundred. 20, Refer. 21, Infer. 25, All.

PUZZLE No. 114

Across: 1, Round the clock. 8, Used. 9, Bag. 10, Rating. 11, Comestible. 13, Amos. 14, Person. 16, Lifeless. 19, Eighteen. 22, Ambush. 25, Adam. 26, Trade union. 27, Sorrel. 28, Ann. 29, Acid. 30, Second helping.

Down: 1, Restore. 2, Undress. 3, Debutante. 4, Hog. 5, Carve. 6, Outfall. 7, Kinross. 12, Belinda. 15, Rag. 17, Fraternal. 18, Emu. 20, Indoors. 21, Homeric. 23, Bengali. 24, Snowing. 26, Talon. 28, Ash.

PUZZLE No. 115

Across: 1, Embarrassing. 8, Rattans. 9, Cutlass. 11, Thickening. 12, Mere. 14, Basement. 16, Bottle. 17, Tar. 19, Rebate. 21, Peekaboo.

24, Nail. 25, Bimetallic. 27, Extract. 28, Ratable. 29, Tearing hurry.

Down: 1, Entries. 2, Blacksmith. 3, Resonant. 4, Accent. 5, Site. 6, Neatest. 7, Protuberance. 10, Skeleton crew. 13, Dock-master. 15, Tap. 18, Research. 20, Bristle. 22, Ball-boy. 23, Kitten. 26, Fair.

PUZZLE No. 116

Across: 6, Easy come easy go. 9, Albert. 10, Beetroot. 11, Anathema. 13, Bereft. 15, Abacus. 17, Driver. 19, Edward. 20, Ignition. 22, Balmoral. 24, Taught. 26, Close attention.

Down: 1, Decline and fall. 2, Esme. 3, Scythe. 4, December. 5, User. 7, Mob-law. 8, Good-for-nothing. 12, Tiara. 14, Rivet. 16, Underlay. 18, Fillet. 21, Noting. 23, Mast. 25, Unit.

PUZZLE No. 117

Across: 1, Wardrobe. 5, Atomic. 9, Compound. 10, Cronin. 12, Etna. 13, Racecourse. 15, Leather-jacket. 19, Power politics. 23, Terracotta. 25, Flea. 28, Foeman. 29, Triangle. 30, Liking. 31, Imitator.

Down: 1, Wicker. 2, Roman. 3, Riot. 4, Beneath. 6, Torso. 7, Mandrakes. 8, Concerto. 11, Peer. 14, Pair. 15, Lower deck. 16, Eel. 17, Axis. 18, Spiteful. 20, Oboe. 21, Interim. 22, Career. 24, Again. 26, Light. 27, Part.

PUZZLE No. 118

Across: 1, Package deal. 9, Cabaret. 10, Emerges. 11, Oar. 12, Edition. 13, Gristle. 14, Mar. 15, Yeast. 17, Games. 18, Allow. 20, Ducat. 22, Tea. 24, Cottage. 25, Cruiser. 26, Sal. 27, Stories. 28, Actuary. 29, Street scene.

Down: 1, Public relations. 2, Certify. 3, Alton. 4, Energetic. 5, Evening. 6, Legitimate stage. 7, Scream. 8, Assess. 16, Addressee. 18, Access. 19, Wearier. 21, Trustee. 23, Arrays. 25, Class.